HEALING WITH COLOUR

This series introduces a wide range of healing techniques that can be used either independently or as a complement to traditional medical treatment. Most of the techniques included in the series can be learnt and practised alone, and each encourages a degree of self-reliance, offering the tools needed to achieve and maintain an optimum state of health.

Each title opens with information on the history and principles of the technique and goes on to offer practical and straightforward guidance on ways in which it can be applied, with diagrams and case studies where appropriate. Please note that readers are advised to seek professional guidance for serious ailments, and to make use of the list of practitioners for further guidance. Many of the techniques in this series are taught in workshops and adult education classes; all of the titles are written by professional practitioners with many years of experience and proven track records.

AVAILABLE IN THIS SERIES
Healing with Herbs — Judith Hoad
Healing with Homeopathy — Peter Chappell and David Andrews
Healing with Meditation — Doriel Hall
Healing with Osteopathy — Peta Sneddon and Paolo Coseschi
Healing with Reflexology — Rosalind Oxenford

FORTHCOMING TITLES IN THIS SERIES
Healing with Ayurveda
Healing with Chinese Medicine
Healing with Crystals
Healing with Essential Oils
Healing with Feng Shui
Healing with Flower Essences
Healing with Nutritional Therapy
Healing with Shiatsu

Healing with Colour

HELEN GRAHAM

Gill & Macmillan

Gill & Macmillan Ltd
Goldenbridge
Dublin 8
with associated companies throughout the world
© Helen Graham 1996
0 7171 2422 3
Series editor: Tessa Strickland
Series copy editor: Pamela Dix
Illustrations by Katherine Armitage
Index compiled by Helen Litton
Print origination by Typeform Repro Ltd, Dublin
Printed by ColourBooks Ltd, Dublin

A catalogue record is available for this book from the
British Library.

1   3   5   4   2

Contents

PART ONE

The Uses of Colour in Healing

CHAPTER ONE

The History of Healing with Colour

'Let there be light: and there was light.'
(Genesis 1:3)

In the early 1970s Lindsey, a friend of mine, took part in a unique experiment. With her husband, three young sons and ten other people she was selected from several thousand applicants to live for twelve months in a reconstructed Iron Age settlement, so that archaeologists, anthropologists and social historians could test various theories about patterns of living some 2,000 years ago. Lindsey told me that one of the things she and her companions had missed most was colour. Living in a dark hut in a small forest clearing had made them aware of its importance to everyday life. They craved it so much that they attempted, unsuccessfully, to put some colour into their drab lives by producing dyes. Long-term hostages such as Brian Keenan have also described a similar craving, and their relief at being able to glimpse the colour of the sky.

Those who have never been deprived of colour tend to take it for granted, and generally don't realise its importance to our health and well-being. Nevertheless it is a basic need. Our early ancestors realised this, and the ancient healing traditions of many cultures reflect this awareness. The use of colour in healing is not new. Colour therapy, as it is now called, represents the rediscovery of some of the principles and practices known since the earliest times.

BECOMING ENLIGHTENED

For ancient man light was seen as sustaining life and all the functions and processes of living things. 'En-lightenment' was therefore synonymous with health in its literal sense of wholeness or holiness of body, mind and spirit. For the ancients, light was essentially a spiritual as well as a physical phenomenon.

In many ancient cultures the sun was worshipped. The most important aim of life was for man to realise the light and thereby God. Ancient magic attempted to achieve this connection by 'bringing down the light', transferring and reflecting its power. Magic and religion were thus inextricably linked with each other and with medicine.

LIGHT AND COLOUR

Light is a narrow band of visible energy in the middle of a spectrum that embraces energies from cosmic rays to radio waves. These energies can be graded according to wavelength and measured in nanometres, each equivalent to one millionth of a millimetre. The spectrum of visible light falls within 380–760 mm. Each variation in wavelength within this band of energy can be sensed by our eyes and interpreted as a specific colour. Reds have the longest wavelength, lowest frequency and least energy, while violets have the shortest wavelength, highest frequencies and the most energy. Beyond the red end of the visible spectrum there are the longer wavelengths of infrared radiation, microwaves and radio waves; beyond the violet end there are shorter wavelengths of ultraviolet radiation, X-rays, gamma rays and cosmic rays. The energy of sunlight produces all the wavelengths of colour from ultraviolet through the visual spectrum to infrared in a roughly equal distribution. This is known as full-spectrum white light.

The effects of colour on life must have been of great significance to early human beings, whose very existence was governed by light and darkness. Most living things appear to be vitalised by the bright reds, oranges and yellows of daylight and calmed and rejuvenated by the blues, indigos and violets of the night. For the ancients, the colours that make up sunlight were each considered to show a different aspect of the divine, and to influence different qualities of life. Colour is therefore an important feature in the symbolism of ancient cultures throughout the world, and the origins of healing with colour in western civilisation can be traced back to the mythology of Ancient Egypt and Greece.

HEALING WITH COLOUR IN THE ANCIENT WORLD

According to Ancient Egyptian mythology, the art of healing with founded by the god Thoth. He was known to the Ancient Greeks as Hermes Trismegistus, literally 'Hermes thrice-greatest', because he was also credited with various works on mysticism and magic. Teachings attributed to him included the use of colour in healing, and in the Hermetic tradition the Ancient Egyptians and Greeks used coloured minerals, stones, crystals, salves and dyes as remedies, and in treatment sanctuaries painted in various shades.

Interest in the physical nature of colour developed in Ancient Greece alongside the concept of the elements — air, fire, water and earth. These fundamental constituents of the universe were associated with the qualities of coldness, heat, wetness and dryness, and also with four humours or bodily fluids — choler or yellow bile, (red) blood, (white) phlegm, and melancholy or black bile. These were thought to arise in four organs — the spleen, heart, liver and brain — and to determine emotional and physical disposition. Health involved the proper balance of these humours, and disease their mixture in wrong proportion. Colour was intrinsic to healing, which involved restoring the balance. Coloured garments, oils, plasters, ointments and salves were used to treat disease.

By the end of the classical period in Greece, these principles were included in the scientific framework that was to remain largely unchanged in the west until the Middle Ages. In the first century A.D., Aurelius Cornelius Celsus followed the doctrines established by Pythagoras and Hippocrates, and included the use of coloured ointments, plasters and flowers in several treatises on medicine.

HEALING WITH COLOUR DURING THE MIDDLE AGES

With the coming of Christianity, however, all that was pagan was exorcised, including the healing practices of the Egyptians, Greeks and Romans. The progress of medicine throughout Europe was effectively halted while those who clung to traditional principles and practices of healing were persecuted. The ancient healing arts, preserved only by secret oral tradition passed on to the initiates, thus became hidden or 'occult'.

It was an Arab physician and disciple of Aristotle, Avicenna (980–*circa* 1037), who advanced the art of healing. In his *Canon of Medicine* he made clear the vital importance of colour in both diagnosis and treatment. Avicenna noted that colour was an observable symptom of disease, and so he developed a chart which related colour to temperament and the physical condition of the body. He used colour in treatment, insisting that red moved the blood, blue or white cooled it and yellow reduced pain and inflammation, prescribing potions of red flowers to cure blood disorders, and yellow flowers and morning sunlight to cure disorders of the biliary system.

Avicenna wrote also of the possible dangers of colour in treatment, observing that a person with a nose-bleed, for example, should not gaze at things of a brilliant red colour or be exposed to red light, as this would stimulate the sanguineous humour, whereas blue would soothe it and reduce blood flow.

The Renaissance saw a resurgence in the art of healing in Europe. One of the most renowned healers of the period was Theophrastus Bombastus von Hohenheim (1493–1541), known as Paracelsus, who attributed his understanding of the laws and practices of medicine to his conversations with witches (women who were primarily pagan healers purged by the Church).

Paracelsus regarded light and colour as essential for good health, and used them extensively in treatment, together with elixirs, charms and talismans, herbs and minerals. A great exponent of alchemy, Paracelsus insisted that its true purpose was not to make gold but to prepare effective medicines, and he used liquid gold to treat ailments of all kinds, apparently with a good deal of success. Consequently his fame as a great physician spread throughout Europe.

ENLIGHTENMENT, SCIENCE AND HEALING

However, after the Middle Ages Paracelsus and other alchemists lost their prestige as mysticism and magic were overtaken by rationalism and science. By the eighteenth century, 'enlightenment' had taken on a new meaning. It was the name given to a philosophical movement that stressed the importance of reason and the critical appraisal of existing ideas. Reason dictated that all knowledge had to be certain and evident; anything about which there could be doubt was rejected. As a result the divine gradually disappeared from the scientific world view.

By the nineteenth century the emphasis in science was exclusively on the material rather than the spiritual. As medicine came under the umbrella of science it too focused on the material physical body, ignoring the mind and spirit. With the advent of physical medicine, and such treatments as surgery and antiseptics, interest in healing with colour declined. It didn't resurface until the nineteenth century, and then not in Europe but North America.

In 1876 Augustus Pleasanton published *Blue and Sun-lights,* in which he reported his findings on the effects of colour in plants, animals and humans. He claimed that the quality, yield and size of grapes could be significantly increased if they were grown in greenhouses with alternating blue and transparent panes of glass. He also reported having cured certain diseases, increased fertility and the rate of physical maturation in animals by exposing them to blue light. Pleasanton also maintained that blue light was effective in treating human diseases and pain. His work gained supporters, but was dismissed by the medical establishment as unscientific.

However, in 1877 a distinguished physician, Dr Seth Pancoast, published *Blue and Red Lights,* in which he too advocated the use of colour in healing.

Edwin Babbit's *The Principles of Light and Colour* was published in 1878; the second edition, published in 1896, attracted worldwide attention. Babbit advanced a comprehensive theory of healing with colour. He identified the colour red as a stimulant, notably of blood and to a lesser extent the nerves; yellow and orange as nerve stimulants; blue and violet as soothing to all systems and with anti-inflammatory properties. Accordingly Babbit prescribed red for paralysis, consumption, physical exhaustion and chronic rheumatism; yellow as a laxative, emetic and purgative and for bronchial difficulties; blue for inflammatory conditions, sciatica, meningitis, nervous headache, irritability and sunstroke. Babbit developed various devices, including a special cabinet called the Thermolume, which used coloured glass and natural light to produce coloured light; and the Chromo Disk, a funnel-shaped device fitted with special colour filters that could localise light onto various parts of the body.

Babbit established the correspondence between colours and minerals, which he used as an addition to treatment with coloured light, and developed elixirs by irradiating water with sunlight filtered through coloured lenses. He claimed that this 'potentised' water retained the energy of the vital elements within the particular colour filter used, and that it had remarkable healing power. Solar tinctures of this kind are still made and used today by many colour therapists.

Chromopaths then sprang up throughout the USA and Britain, and they developed extensive colour prescriptions for every conceivable ailment. By the end of the last century, red light was used to prevent scars forming in cases of smallpox, and startling cures were later reported among tuberculosis patients exposed to sunlight and ultraviolet rays. Nevertheless, the medical profession remained sceptical of any claims made for healing with colour.

TWENTIETH-CENTURY SCIENCE AND HEALING WITH COLOUR

Investigations into the therapeutic uses of colour were carried out in Europe during the early twentieth century, notably by Rudolph Steiner, who related colour to form, shape and sound. He suggested that the vibrational quality of certain colours is amplified by some forms, and that certain combinations of colour and shape have either destructive or regenerative effects on living organisms. In the schools inspired by Steiner's work, classrooms are painted and textured to correspond to the 'mood' of children at various stages of their development.

Rudolph Steiner's work was continued by Theo Gimbel, who established the Hygeia Studios and College of Colour Therapy in Britain. Among the principles explored by Gimbel are the claims of Max Lüscher, a former Professor of Psychology at Basle University, who claimed that colour preferences demonstrate states of mind and/or glandular imbalance, and can be used as the basis for physical and psychological diagnosis. Lüscher's theory, which forms the basis of the Lüscher Colour Test, rests on the idea that the significance of colour for man originates in his early history, when his behaviour was governed by night and day. Lüscher believed that the colours associated with these two environments — yellow and dark blue — are connected with differences in metabolic rate and glandular secretions appropriate to the energy required for night-time sleep and daytime hunting. He also believed that autonomic (involuntary) responses are associated with other colours.

Support for Lüscher's theories was provided in the 1940s, by the Russian scientist S.V. Krakov, who established that the colour red stimulates the sympathetic part of the autonomic nervous system, while blue stimulates the parasympathetic part. His findings were confirmed in 1958 by Robert Gerard of the USA.

Gerard found that red was disturbing to anxious or tense subjects, while blue had a calming effect. Red produced feelings of arousal and blue produced feelings of calm, tranquillity and well-being. The discovery that blood pressure increases under red light and decreases under blue light led Gerard to suggest that psychophysiological activation increases with wavelength from blue to red.

Although cautious about his findings and insisting on the need for further research, Gerard highlighted the possible therapeutic benefits of the colour blue, and recommended it as supplementary therapy in the treatment of various conditions. Among other suggestions, Gerard pointed to the possible uses of blue as a tranquilliser and relaxant in anxious individuals and as a way of reducing blood pressure in the treatment of hypertension.

Dr Harry Wohlfarth also showed that certain colours have measurable and predictable effects on the autonomic nervous system of people. In numerous studies, he found that blood pressure and pulse and respiration rates increase most under yellow light, moderately under orange and minimally under red; while decreasing most under black, moderately under blue and minimally under green.

Subsequent research on plants and animals conducted by the photobiologist Dr John Ott also demonstrated the effects of colour on growth and development. Plants grown under red glass were found to shoot up four times quicker than those grown in ordinary sunlight, and to grow much more slowly under green glass. However, although red light initially overstimulated plants, their growth was subsequently stunted, whereas blue light produced slower growth initially but taller, thicker plants later.

Rodents kept under blue plastic grew normally, but when kept under red or pink plastic their appetite and growth rate increased. If kept under blue light animals grew denser coats.

During the 1950s, studies suggested that neonatal jaundice, a potentially fatal condition found in two-thirds of premature babies, could be successfully treated by exposure to sunlight. This was confirmed in the 1960s, and white light replaced the high-risk blood transfusions in the treatment of this condition. Blue light was later found to be more effective and less hazardous than full-spectrum light, now the most common form of treatment for neonatal jaundice.

Bright white full-spectrum light is also now being used in the treatment of cancers, seasonal affective disorder (so-called 'winter depression'), anorexia and bulimia nervosa, insomnia, jet lag, shift-working, alcohol and drug dependency and to reduce overall levels of medication.

The blue light found to be successful in the treatment of neonatal jaundice has also been shown to be effective in the treatment of rheumatoid arthritis. In studies by McDonald, most of those exposed to blue light for variable periods up to fifteen minutes experienced a significant degree of pain relief. It was concluded that the pain reduction was directly related both to the blue light and the length of exposure to it. Blue light is also used in healing injured tissue and preventing scar tissue, in the treatment of cancers and non-malignant tumours and skin and lung conditions.

In 1990 scientists reported to the annual conference of the American Association of the Advancement of Science on the successful use of blue light in the treatment of a wide variety of psychological problems, including addictions, eating disorders, impotence and depression.

RECENT APPLICATIONS OF COLOUR TO HEALING

At the other end of the colour spectrum, red light has been shown to be effective in the treatment of migraine headaches and cancer. As a result, colour is becoming widely accepted as a therapeutic tool with various medical applications. A new technique, which has been developed in the USA over the past two decades as a result of pioneering research, is photodynamic therapy, or PDT. This is based on the discovery that certain intravenously injected photosensitive chemicals not only accumulate in cancer cells but selectively identify these cells under ultraviolet light. These photosensitive chemicals then exclusively destroy the cancer cells when activated by red light, whose longer wavelength allows it to penetrate tissue more deeply than other colours. PDT can be used for both diagnosis and treatment. Dr Thomas Dougherty, who developed PDT, reports that in a worldwide experiment more than 3,000 people with a wide variety of malignant tumours have been successfully treated with this technique.

OTHER THERAPEUTIC APPLICATIONS OF COLOUR

Colour is also used therapeutically in a variety of non-medical settings. In some cases its effects have been quite accidental, as in a report to me by the governor of a newly-built prison in which each of its four wings had been painted in a different colour. Both he and his staff found that the behaviour of the prisoners varied significantly depending on which wing they lived in, although their allocation to each had been random. Those in red and yellow wings were more inclined to violence than those in the blue and green wings.

Experimental research lends support to these observations. Viewing red light has been found to increase subjects' strength by 13.5 per cent and to elicit 5.8 per cent more electrical activity in the arm muscles. For this reason it is now used to improve the performance of athletes. Whereas red light appears to help athletes who need short, quick bursts of energy, blue light assists in performances requiring a more steady energy output.

By comparison, pink has been found to have a tranquillising and calming effect within minutes of exposure. It suppresses hostile, aggressive and anxious behaviour — interesting given its traditional association with women in western culture. Pink holding cells are now widely used to reduce violent and aggressive behaviour among prisoners, and some sources have reported a reduction of muscle strength in inmates within 2.7 seconds. It appears that when in pink surroundings people cannot be aggressive even if they want to, because the colour saps their energy.

By contrast, yellow should be avoided in such contexts as it is highly stimulating. Gimbel has suggested a possible relationship between violent street crime and sodium yellow street lighting.

Research has also shown that colour tinted spectacles can be highly effective in the treatment of learning difficulties, notably dyslexia. This was first discovered by American psychologist Helen Irlen, but was regarded sceptically until recent investigations by the British Medical Research Council confirmed Irlen's claims. In June 1993, a new optician's device called the Intuitive Colorimeter was made available to British opticians so they could measure which tint — bright pink, yellow, green or blue — best helps people who normally see text as swirling, wobbling or with letters appearing in the wrong order.

CONTEMPORARY UNDERSTANDING OF THE PHYSICAL EFFECTS OF COLOUR

Until recently the function of light was thought to relate largely to sight. However, it is now well established that colour need not actually be seen for it to have definite psychological and physiological effects. It can also be distinguished by blind, colour-blind and blind-folded subjects. This phenomenon, referred to as eyeless sight, dermo-optic vision or bio-introscopy, has been researched since the 1920s, when it was established that hypnotised blind-folded subjects could recognise colours and shapes with their foreheads, and that non-hypnotised blind-folded subjects could precisely describe colours and shapes presented under glass.

Research in Russia during the 1960s was stimulated by studies of Roza Kulesheva, who when blind-folded could distinguish colour and shape with her fingertips, and could also read in this way. Other experiments found that Kulesheva was not exceptional; one in six experimental subjects could recognise colour with their fingertips after only 20–30 minutes training, and blind people developed this sensitivity even more quickly.

Some subjects who could distinguish colour correctly by holding their fingers 20–80 cm above colour cards described experiencing sensations varying from needle pricks to faint breezes, depending on the colour. Even when heat differences, structural differences in dyestuffs and other variables were controlled, people were still able to distinguish colours accurately, whether they were put under glass, tracing paper, aluminium foil, brass or copper plates. The phenomenon remains something of a puzzle.

Understanding of these effects has come about only as a result of research into the hormones melatonin and serotonin, both of which are produced by the pineal gland in the brain. Melatonin is known to be the crucial chemical pathway by which animals respond to light and synchronise their bodily functioning with diurnal, lunar and seasonal variations. Serotonin is a very important neurotransmitter in the brain, whose action has been linked with mental disturbances such as schizophrenia and hallucinogenic states.

Serotonin is produced by day and is a stimulant, whereas the output of melatonin — which is linked with sleep — increases when it is dark and has a generally depressive effect. This is reversed when it is light and production of melatonin drops. Its main site of action appears to be the hypothalamus, the part of the brain involved in mediating the effects of various hormones and regulating emotions. However, changes in the output of melatonin in response to light influence every cell of the body, notably the reproductive processes, which are very sensitive to such variations. Very high levels of melatonin have been found in women with ovulation problems and anorexia nervosa — a characteristic feature of which is amenorrhoea, or absence of periods; in men with low sperm count; and people suffering from seasonal affective disorder, which usually occurs during winter.

Depression in general appears to be closely linked with melatonin levels, and sufferers tend to show rapid improvement in response to natural sunlight or light therapy using full-spectrum lamps. Research has also confirmed that certain parts of the brain are not only light sensitive but actually respond differently to different wavelengths; it is now believed that different wavelengths (colour) of radiation interact differently with the endocrine system to stimulate or reduce hormone production.

So it might be thought that modern-day healing with colour is based on the discoveries of western science over the past few decades. However, it is based on an altogether more ancient and esoteric science whose principles and practices have yet to be acknowledged, much less verified by western scientists. Healing with colour is rooted in ancient mysticism, the major principles of which are common to many different cultures throughout the world.

CHAPTER TWO

The Principles of Healing with Colour

'You are light.'
(Luke 11:34)

In mystic traditions, all objects — living or not — are
seen as possessing other bodies invisible to normal sight.
These envelop the physical body and act as a medium
for the interplay of subtle energies in the immediate
environment. St Paul expressed such a view, claiming that
'there is a natural body and a physical body' (Corinthians
15:44). The former was called a halo by early Christians,
and shown as a hazy coloured light enveloping the entire
body, but in later Renaissance and medieval art it was
confined to the head region.

Variously referred to as the Ka in Ancient Egypt; the
aura in Ancient Greece; the *döppelganger* in medieval
Europe; the vital body in certain Rosicrucian schools; the
astral, etheric body or double in other western occult
traditions; the perispirit in French spiritism and the linga
sharirah in the east, this phenomenon was considered
synonymous with the spirit or soul, and as surviving death.
Together, these individual energy bodies were thought to
make up the universal energy field.

TRADITIONAL VIEWS OF THE
HUMAN ENERGY FIELD

Mystics consider that subtle energies from the
environment are distributed through the body by way of
several major power centres on the surface of the
non-physical counterpart, or energy body. These are

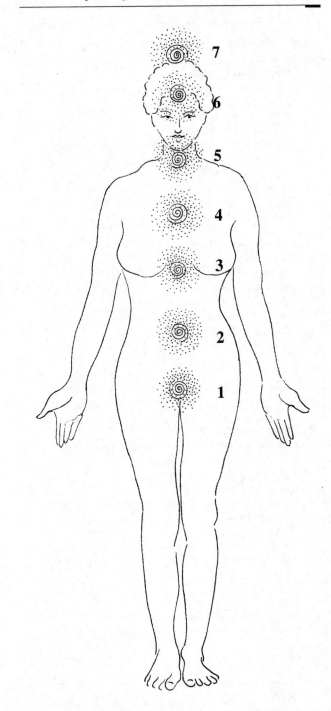

Key to illustration:

1. **Base Chakra**
   Location: base of spine
   Colour: red
   Endocrine: ovaries, testes
   Oils: myrrh, vetivert, patchouli
   Gems/Minerals: ruby, garnet, bloodstone, red jasper,
     smoky quartz, black tourmaline
   Foods: proteins, red fruits/vegetables
   Qualities: security, grounding, stability, health, courage
   Negative Qualities: self-centredness, insecurity, anger,
     violence

2. **Navel Chakra (Hara)**
   Location: navel area
   Colour: orange
   Endocrine: adrenal glands
   Oils: sandalwood, cardomum, ginger
   Gems/Minerals: carnelian, coral, gold calcite, amber,
     citrine, gold topaz, peach aventurine
   Foods: yellow fruits/vegetables
   Qualities: gut instincts, emotions, sexuality, exercise,
     movement
   Negative Qualities: over-indulgence, sexual difficulties,
     envy, bladder/uterine disorders

3. **Solar Plexus Chakra**
   Location: approximately 2 ins above navel
   Colour: yellow
   Endocrine: pancreas, adrenal glands, liver
   Oils: lemon, citronella
   Gems/Minerals: citrine, gold, gold topaz, amber, tiger's
     eye, gold calcite
   Foods: yellow fruits/vegetables
   Qualities: intellect, rationality, will, personal power
   Negative Qualities: abuse of power, anger, fear, hate, stress
     disorders, digestive problems

4. **Heart Chakra**
   Location: centre of chest
   Colour: green
   Endocrine: thymus gland
   Oils: pine, bergamot, invila, melissa

Gems/Minerals: emerald, beryl, green tourmaline, jade, agate, malachite, green aventurine, rose quartz, rhodochrosite

Foods: green fruits/vegetables

Qualities: unconditional love, compassion, forgiveness, understanding, balance, openness, touch, sensitivity, immunity

Negative Qualities: resentment, insensitivity, imbalance, heart and circulation problems, rheumatism

5. **Throat Chakra**

Location: centre of throat

Colour: sky blue

Endocrine: thyroid gland

Oils: lavender, camomile, geranium

Gems/Minerals: turquoise, crysocolla, blue topaz, sodalite, lapis lazuli, aquamarine, kyanite

Foods: blue fruit/vegetables, asparagus

Qualities: speech, communication, creative expression

Negative Qualities: speech and communication problems, thyroid dysfunction

6. **Brow Chakra (Third Eye)**

Location: centre of forehead

Colour: indigo (dark blue)

Endocrine: pineal gland

Oils: patchouli, frankincense

Gems/Minerals: lapis lazuli, azuri, sodalite, sapphire

Foods: purple/blue fruits/vegetables

Qualities: soul realisation, intuition, insight, imagination, clairvoyance, concentration

Negative Qualities: lack of concentration, cynicism, headaches, bad dreams, detachment from reality

7. **Crown Chakra**

Location: top of head

Colour: violet

Endocrine: pituitary gland

Oils: elemi, frankincense

Gems/Minerals: amethyst, alexandrite, sugalite, purple fluorite, selenite

Foods: purple fruits/vegetables

Qualities: union with higher self, the infinite, spirituality, higher consciousness

Negative Qualities: alienation, despair, confusion

described as three-dimensional pulsating vortices that appear to seers or clairvoyants like funnels, trumpets or convolvulus flowers and rotate rhythmically from the mid-point outwards rather like catherine wheels. According to the direction of spin, the wheels either draw energy into or direct it out of the body, vitalising or enervating it.

Much was written about these centres in Ancient Hindu texts. The Theosophists, who first wrote about them in English in the late nineteenth and early twentieth centuries, retained the Sanskrit term *chakra,* meaning wheel, to refer to them. Early European mystics were also familiar with them, and ancient knowledge of the chakras in the west is suggested in the symbolism of Ancient Egyptian monuments and Freemasonry. Similar ideas are found in the traditional wisdom of North and Central American Indians, the Eskimo and the Tibetans. Within these different traditions, though, the number and location of the chakras varies.

THE CHAKRAS

The Hindu locate seven major chakras along the vertical axis of the energy body, corresponding with the spine in the physical body, and a number of minor chakras elsewhere on its surface. According to ancient wisdom, energy in the form of light is drawn into the body's immaterial counterpart, which acts as a prism, breaking it down into seven streams corresponding with the frequency bands of the colour spectrum. Each of these is drawn through resonance to a chakra whose vibrations are of the same frequency. These vibrations become progressively more dense, heavy and lower in frequency along the vertical axis of the body. At its base they merge with and arise from earth energies, represented in Indian thought as a coiled serpent — Kundalini — and in Chinese thought by a dragon. The upward spiral motion of these energies around the central axis of the spine is also represented in the caduceus, the traditional symbol of the healing arts in Ancient Greece, which is still retained as the emblem of modern western medicine.

The chakras, which may be thought of as transmitters or transformers of energy, are believed to vibrate at a characteristic frequency as they distribute energy throughout the body. The energy patterns around each chakra, although always changing, are mostly of a certain colour whose vibrations correspond with its basic frequency. The prevailing colour of a chakra indicates how well its energies are being transformed and transmitted at a given time and therefore reflect current experience.

In ancient traditions each chakra is also associated with a musical note, a symbolic form and certain elements of the same characteristic vibrational frequency (which vary according to the tradition). Certain traditions also assign planets to the chakras, suggesting that they are sensitive to planetary influence and providing a physical basis for astrology. Recently the chakras have also been associated with the location and functioning of the major nerve plexuses of the body, each of which is connected to one of the glands of the endocrine system. So the slightest imbalance of energy in any chakra is thought to influence the corresponding gland, giving rise to fluctuations in hormones which are secreted directly into the bloodstream, producing immediate changes in mood, appearance, tension, respiration, digestion, intuition and intelligence. The correct and balanced action of these seven chakras is expressed as absolute and perfect health on all levels.

The principal features of the human chakra system common to many traditions are as follows.

The first, root or base chakra known in Sanskrit as *Muladhara,* and located at a position corresponding with the base of the spine, is the first manifestation of the life force in the physical body. Its functioning determines the person's level of physical energy and the will to live in physical reality. It is concerned with basic survival and physical health; and being intimately connected with the prostate and testes in men and the uterus in women, it influences sexual activity and regulates creativity. This energy primarily affects the legs, the hip joints and base of the spine, overlapping into the pelvic area, providing the strength to support the physical body and influencing safety and security. However, the coccyx functions on the etheric level as a pump, directing the flow of energy up the spine and connecting each chakra with the life force.

Psychologically, the first chakra is associated with feelings of being securely grounded, 'well rooted' and belonging. It is thought to be mostly red, influenced by Saturn, associated with the element earth, the symbolic form of the square, the metal lead (base metal), the sense of smell and the sound vibration LA. (The symbols and sounds included here and below are from the Tantric tradition.)

The second or sacral chakra, Svadhistana, located in the pelvic region midway between the pubis and the navel, is considered in traditional systems to be the centre of sexual activity. Because sexuality is an expression of the life force this chakra is closely related to the base chakra, and influences physical and sexual vitality. It is situated in the region referred to as the gut or belly, which the Japanese term the *hara,* and is associated with the liver, pancreas, spleen, kidneys and bladder, and therefore with metabolism, digestion, detoxification, immunity to disease, and the balance of fluids and sugars within the body. It is also thought to have glandular connections with the testes and ovaries, and to influence the production of the hormones testosterone and oestrogen.

On the psychological level it relates to passions or 'gut feelings' and emotions, and to issues people care deeply about — power, sex and material wealth. It is associated with the colour orange, the influence of Jupiter, water, tin, the sense of taste, the symbolic form of a pyramid with its capstone removed, and the sound BA.

The third or solar plexus chakra, Manipura, positioned slightly above the navel, is thought of as the centre of personal power or the power to act, and therefore with the sense of vision. It is associated with the adrenal glands, which through the production of adrenalin profoundly affect the sympathetic nervous system, and thereby muscular energy, heartbeat, digestion, circulation and mood.

Traditionally it is related to mental functioning — the intellect or rational mind, intentionality and will — but it is also directly related to the second chakra and so to emotional life. Thought to be primarily yellow, it is associated with Mars, fire, iron, sight, the symbolic form of the circle, and the sound RA.

The fourth or heart chakra, Anahata, found in the centre of the chest over the breast bone, is believed to relate to the thymus gland situated behind the sternum, the main function of which in adults is to create immunity to disease. Traditionally it is associated with love and compassion, feeling, sensitivity, touch, the skin and the hands, and with the colour green. Interestingly it is known that many of the body's immune cells are located in the skin and can be stimulated by touch. It is thought to be influenced by Venus, associated with air, copper, the symbol of the equilateral cross, and the two-syllable sound YA Mn.

The fifth or throat chakra, Vishuddhi, located at the front of the throat, is thought to influence the thyroid gland, which affects the metabolism, musculature and heat control of the body. Traditionally it relates to communication and self-expression, to hearing and taking responsibility for one's personal needs. It is associated with sky blue, the planet Mercury, ether, hearing, the symbolic form of the chalice, and the sound HA.

The sixth or brow chakra, Ajna, found just above and between the eyebrows in the centre of the forehead, is traditionally known as the 'third eye' and is identified with visual imagery, insight, intuitive understanding, clairvoyance, psychic abilities and ecstasy. It is associated with the pineal gland, which according to contemporary research has a significant role in processing mental imagery and unconscious processes, and is also responsible for the production of the hormones melatonin and serotonin. Its colour is midnight blue or indigo, and its symbols are the moon, gold and silver, the six-pointed star, and the sound AH.

The seventh or crown chakra, Sahasrara, is positioned in the centre of the upper skull; traditionally regarded as the seat of the soul, it is identified with pure or enlightened being, spirituality and integration of the whole being. It is associated with the pituitary, the master endocrine gland, which regulates the functioning of the other glands, and is closely associated with the pineal gland. Its colour is purple or violet, symbolised by the thousand-petalled lotus and the sacred sound OM (oh aa um), which is considered to be the total amalgam of all sound and of all creation.

According to the chakra system, man has a seven-fold nature. The first and second chakras are mostly concerned with receiving and distributing physical energies, and combine to give a person potency, virility and the will to live. The third, fourth and fifth chakras are concerned with psychological energies and so with personality rather than physical traits; the sixth and seventh chakras with spiritual energies which are an expression of the individual's relationship to his spirit or soul.

The chakras function as an integrated system, rather than in isolation. If one begins to malfunction, so will others, as they attempt to compensate for reduced energy transmission in one centre by working overtime. So the chakra system provides the impetus for the regulated, balanced flow of energy throughout the whole person which is necessary for health.

THE AURA

Traditionally the flow of energy is not confined within the physical body as this is normally thought of. In the ancient view, the body emits a radiant energy which relates specifically to the location and intensity of energy within it, and therefore reveals something about how it is functioning.

**A TWO - DIMENSIONAL REPRESENTATION OF THE HUMAN AURA
SHOWING EACH BAND AS IT RELATES TO SPECIFIC CHAKRAS**

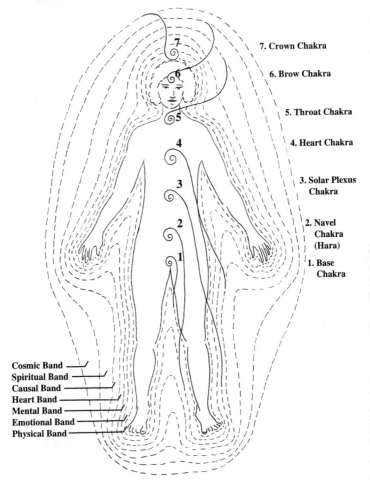

7. Crown Chakra

6. Brow Chakra

5. Throat Chakra

4. Heart Chakra

3. Solar Plexus Chakra

2. Navel Chakra (Hara)

1. Base Chakra

Cosmic Band
Spiritual Band
Causal Band
Heart Band
Mental Band
Emotional Band
Physical Band

This three-dimensional emanation, which surrounds the body in all directions and extends for some distance beyond its surface, is widely referred to as the aura, and represents the sum total of the energy emitted by the chakras.

Normally invisible but discernible by seers and clairvoyants — who since the earliest times have described it as a large shimmering oval, comprising a mass of fine bright fibres or rays arranged in seven bands, each corresponding to the functioning of a chakra — the aura reveals the physical, psychological and spiritual well-being of the person it envelops.

When the chakras are functioning normally, each will 'open' by spinning clockwise and drawing energy in from the universal energy field to distribute throughout the body. When the transmission of energy has occurred, the colour originating from each should be very pale and translucent.

However, when the chakra spins anti-clockwise it remains closed to incoming energies, which consequently are not distributed within the body and show themselves as darker, more dense patches or blotches of colour in the aura. The space between the body and the first colour emanation of the aura is referred to as the ovum. It is not 'empty' as such, being the most dense and therefore most easily visible part of the energy field, but is colourless or a dull white/bold, so appearing to be blank.

The first layer of the aura, the health band, emanates from the base chakra and reflects the overall vitality of the physical body. It is traditionally described in metaphysical literature as red. The second band of the aura, known as the emotional or astral band, emanates from the second chakra. It reflects physical and sexual activity, and 'gut feelings', and is orange in colour. The third layer of the

aura, the mental band, comes from the solar plexus chakra
and reflects mental functions based on the intellect and
personal power. It is yellow, and shiny or brilliant in a
mentally alive person. The fourth layer of the aura, or heart
band, emanates from the heart chakra. It is green and
reflects inspiration in all forms. The fifth layer of the aura,
or causal band, comes from the throat chakra and is blue,
reflecting self-expression and the karma of the soul — its
progress through successive incarnations. The dark blue
sixth layer, or spiritual band, emanates from the sixth
chakra, reflecting the person's spiritual development and
intuitive awareness; and the seventh layer, or cosmic band,
reflects the soul principle or cosmic consciousness of the
individual. It is purple in colour.

Each band radiates different colours of varying
intensity that reveal to those who can discern them the
person's state of health, character, emotional disposition
and tendencies, abilities, attitudes, past problems and
spiritual development. The aura can therefore be used for
diagnosis, and throughout history seers (or sensitives) have
reported using it as a basis for healing.

A study of orthodox western physicians has also
revealed that many diagnose illness through the energy
field they perceive around their patients, or through the
energy vortices connected with the endocrine system.
One practitioner, John Pierrakos, has conducted extensive
research on the phenomenon.

SCIENTIFIC MEASUREMENT OF THE CHAKRA–AURA SYSTEM

While the vital force is self-evident to many healers, it has
eluded scientific measurement until recently. This may be
because its subtle energies can only react with and be

detected by living organisms. When it finds its counterpart in a living being, a detectable reaction results. This, it is claimed, is the basis for healing diagnoses, dowsing and water divining. However, because this force is not easily detected by physical instruments in the orthodox scientific world, it is deemed to have no physical reality.

That science is blinkered by the limitations of its own tools is clear from the history of western research into the human energy field during this century. In 1911, Dr Walter Kilner of St Thomas' Hospital, London, developed a special kind of glass which, he claimed, allowed the aura to be seen objectively. This — and his prediction that it would in future be possible to photograph the aura and use it for more accurate diagnosis of all kinds of illness — was dismissed as fanciful. The views of Dr F.S.C. Northrup of Yale, who proposed the existence of dynamic life fields around living things were similarly rejected, as was the discovery of an energy body possessed by all human beings claimed by Yale professor of anatomy H.S. Burr.

However, during the 1930s developments in high voltage photography by Russian scientists Semyon and Valentina Kirlian, which revealed streams of apparent energy flowing from the fingertips in a manner suggested by traditional aura theory, appeared to fulfil Kilner's predictions. Over the next ten years the Kirlians became convinced that these energy streams reflected the well-being or otherwise of an organism, and this view subsequently gained support from research on plants. During the 1960s another Russian researcher, Leonidov, developed a lightless microphoto which provided further objective evidence for the aura.

Professor Vladimir Inyushin, who developed the Kirlians' research, subsequently described the energy field around living forms as a biological plasma body, claiming — as Burr had done previously — that this is a whole unified organism emitting its own electromagnetic fields, which are the basis of all biological fields.

The chakras have also been the subject of considerable scientific research, most notably by the Japanese professor Hiroshi Motoyama. Commencing his research in the 1960s with studies of psychics and healers, Motoyama developed various sophisticated physiological devices for measuring subtle energies in and around the body. He devised an instrument to determine experimentally the working of the chakras. This measures the electromagnetic fields around the body, and can show by subtle changes in these when a chakra is naturally active or activated by some other means. Motoyama concluded that the energy systems underpinning traditional Chinese and Indian medicine are fundamentally the same, despite differences in terminology.

Until recently much of this pioneering scientific research into the subtle energies of the chakras and aura took place only in Russia and the east. There is now, though, an increasing interest in subtle body and energy systems in the west. Professor Thelma Moss of the Neuropsychiatric Institute of the University of California School of Medicine was the first serious researcher of these phenomena in the USA. Since her pioneering work there have been intensive investigations of these energy systems, most notably at the University of California by Dr Valerie Hunt. In Britain, Professor Dennis Milner at Birmingham University has conducted research into Kirlian photography, and the psychophysiology of the chakra system has been mapped out by Dr Serena Roney-Dougal.

THE CHAKRA–AURA SYSTEM AND HEALTH

In North American and Canada there has been extensive investigation of clairvoyants such as Jack Schwarz and Rosaline Bruyère, who perceive chakra and aura energies and use them in diagnosis and treatment. This research appears to confirm the observations of the ancients.

Disturbances in the energy distribution of the base chakra are found to correspond with lack of physical energy and general ill-health, chronic lower back pain, sciatica, varicose veins and rectal problems — including tumours and cancerous growths.

Energy blockages in the second chakra are generally associated with reduced physical and sexual activity, because the pelvic area is the major source of vitality in the body. Imbalances in this chakra are commonly found with problems in women such as: menstrual difficulties, infertility, vaginal infections, ovarian cysts, endometriosis, tumours and cancers of the female organs; and with impotence and prostate problems in men. In both men and women pelvic and lower back pain, sexual difficulties and disease, slipped discs, bladder and urinary problems, and frequent loss of sexual fluids, commonly occur when this chakra is unstable.

The most common physical conditions associated with disturbances in the energy flow of the third or solar plexus chakra include: arthritis, ulcers and related stomach problems, poor digestion, chronic or acute indigestion, eating disorders such as anorexia and bulimia nervosa, nausea, abnormal appetite, colon and intestinal problems including cancer, pancreatitis and pancreatic cancer, diabetes, kidney and liver problems, hepatitis, gall bladder and adrenal gland disorders, and flu.

When the fourth, or heart, chakra is unstable there

may be cardiac or circulatory abnormalities which commonly result in: heart attack, enlarged heart, congestive heart failure, blocked arteries, asthma, allergies, lung problems including cancer, bronchial difficulties, pneumonia, poor circulation, upper back and shoulder problems.

People with imbalances in the fifth or throat chakra have a tendency towards skin problems and allergies, and as a result of poor detoxification within the body: thyroid conditions, throat infections, sore throat, loss of voice, laryngitis, tonsillitis, cancers of the throat and mouth, problems with the teeth and gums, misalignment of the jaw, curved spine, stiff neck, tension headaches arising from the base of the neck, and swollen glands.

The sixth chakra, or 'third eye', is thought to exert a strong influence on the balanced functioning of the endocrine system, visual functioning, sleep, clarity of mental functions and general energy levels. Instability in this chakra is reflected in: fatigue and tiredness, migraine and tension headache, irritability, anxiety, nervousness and depression, nervous breakdown, psychotic illness including schizophrenia, sleep irregularities, coma, neurological disorders including blindness and deafness, epilepsy and seizures, learning difficulties, brain tumours, stroke and blood clots to the brain.

Instability in the seventh or crown chakra can result in disorders of the nervous system, paralysis, bone problems and debilitating illnesses such as multiple sclerosis.

Taken together, the chakra and aura systems provide a comprehensive and consistent account of the distribution and functioning of subtle energies within and around the body, and a framework for what can be thought of as subtle energy therapies such as those traditionally practised in India, Tibet, China, Japan, among Native American Indians, Aboriginals and the Kahunas of Hawaii. These include ages-old practices such as acupuncture, acupressure or Shiatsu, Ayurvedic medicine, and healing with colour; and more recent practices such as reflexology, cranio-sacral therapy, radionics, polarity therapy and homeopathy.

In all these healing systems disease is viewed as fundamentally spiritual in origin, as an imbalance in the energies of the soul, which shows itself firstly as a conflict or problem at the psychological level and only finally as symptoms of physical illness. These approaches to healing therefore address disease primarily at the spiritual and psychological level, and diagnosis tends to emphasise these energies rather than the physical.

DIAGNOSING DISORDER THROUGH THE AURA AND CHAKRAS

Physicist and healer Barbara Ann Brennan believes that auric diagnosis is especially helpful because 'the aura is really the "missing link" between biology and physical medicine, and psychotherapy. It is the "place" where all emotions, thoughts, memories and behaviour patterns are located,' and reflects the activity of the chakras which represent the psychological patterns evolving in a person's life throughout their development. Barbara Brennan observes that most people react to unpleasant experiences by blocking their feelings. This affects the chakras by restricting a great deal of their energy flow, and inhibits fully balanced psychological functioning. If a child is rejected many times when she tries to give love to others she will probably stop trying to do so, and will therefore repress the inner feelings of love on which her former actions were based. To do this she has to stop or slow down the energy flow through the heart chakra, which will affect its functioning. It may become blocked with stagnant energy, spin irregularly or anti–clockwise, become distorted and eventually result in the development of a physical problem. This same process applies to all the chakras.

CHAKRA DYSFUNCTION AND PSYCHOLOGICAL DISORDER

Brennan and Pierrakos have related chakra dysfunction to psychological disorder, and their analysis generally accords with traditional and more contemporary accounts, the common points of which can be found below.

When the base chakra is functioning normally, you are well-grounded in the here-and-now of physical reality, and have power and vitality or presence, and a strong will to live. Such a person feels secure and grounded. When this chakra is blocked you lack physical vitality and strength, and fail to make a strong impression in the physical world. Such an individual lacks 'presence', is insecure in and threatened by the world, may not feel at home anywhere, and feels alone and unsupported. Motoyama's research reveals that a predominance of energy in this chakra can lead to violent aggression, and that accidents causing sudden injury to the coccyx — the spinal energy pump — can cause an uncontrolled release of energy which may contribute to certain types of psychosis.

Normal functioning of the second or sacral chakra is related to giving and receiving physical and sexual pleasure, the capacity for orgasm, and to strong gut feelings and emotions. However, if the centre is dysfunctional, you will have sexual difficulties, feelings of sexual inadequacy, impotence, lack of orgasm, feelings of low self-esteem and general anxiety. This chakra has also been associated with a passion for money and power. So when it is not working properly, your anxiety about money, material possessions and power may create imbalances in all forms of relationship with the material world. The opening of this chakra is also associated with intuition, uncontrolled psychokinetic phenomena such as poltergeist activity and the development of extra-sensory perception such as precognition and out-of-body experiences.

The third or solar plexus chakra normally empowers a person mentally and emotionally. When it is unstable you may have rapid mood swings, a tendency towards depression and anger at feeling controlled by others, a tendency to victimise and to be highly critical of people, and to fear failure. If under-functioning, this chakra gives rise to anxiety and feelings of disempowerment and submissiveness; if over-functioning it may create aggression and domination of others. Energy dysfunctions in this chakra often result in stress disorders, characterised by excessive adrenalin production, ulcers, nervous disorders or chronic fatigue. When it is blocked, feeling and thinking will not be very clear, decision making will be poor and you may fear taking responsibility for your life, thoughts, feelings, attitudes and personal actions. Clairvoyance and mental telepathy may accompany opening of this chakra.

The more open the fourth or heart chakra, the greater is a person's capacity to love. When functioning well you feel self-love and love for family, friends, children, animals, nature and all life forms on earth. If this chakra is dysfunctional you may be over-excitable, extrovert and ambitious for fame. When blocked, other people may be seen as obstacles to accomplishment and fulfilment of your heart's desires, and resentment and bitterness may arise towards others, who you perceive as receiving more love and attention. A 'broken heart' may result from excessive grief or sorrow. Dysfunctions in this chakra may show themselves in relationship difficulties. These may be addictive and stifling, or alternatively superficial and transitory, with some indifference or even total withdrawal. The development of healing abilities is often associated with the opening of this chakra.

The fifth or throat chakra normally facilitates personal expression or individuality, will-power and creativity. When open, you communicate thoughts, feelings, needs, attitudes and opinions, but if this centre is dysfunctional self-expression is adversely affected, creating relationship difficulties. Dishonesty and lying may occur, and other negative behaviour such as fear of self-assertion, allowing yourself to become victimised by others, and gossiping may develop. Dysfunctions in this chakra may show in the voice and in use of language. If it is under-functioning, you may well have a quiet, muffled or somewhat strangled voice and tend not to speak out or up for yourself. You are likely to swallow the views and opinions of others wholesale rather than develop or express your own. If the chakra is blocked you may experience guilt and blame. If over-functioning your voice may be loud and coarse, as you impose your views on others and project on to them attributes you are unwilling to ascribe to yourself. Clairaudience and awareness of the past, present and future are associated with the opening of this chakra.

The normal functions of the sixth chakra or 'third eye' are associated with clear thinking and imagery, insight and intuition. Anti-clockwise movement of this chakra is associated with confused or negative ideas and images about reality. If the chakra is blocked, imagination is poor and creativity and problem solving are limited. Other behavioural problems associated with blocked energy in this chakra include resistance to self-examination; suppression of intuitive capabilities; rigid thinking; obsessionalism; lack of openness to new ideas or those of others; unwillingness to learn from life experiences and lack of self-awareness or insight. Opening of this chakra enables perception of non-physical reality and spirit entities. Overactivity can result in feelings of possession or paranoia.

When activated, the crown chakra heightens the physical and mental senses, and promotes well-being. It provides a clear focus, and when it is open you experience a state of being which goes beyond the physical world, creating a sense of wholeness, peace, faith and a sense of purpose to life. However, when it is blocked, you become closed to spiritual experience and have little or no understanding of the spiritual experiences of others. You are likely to find life meaningless, to experience negative feelings and thoughts, to lack faith in yourself, to fear self-development and knowledge.

Dysfunction in this chakra can be associated either with messianic inflation (believing you are a messiah) and feelings of omnipotence; or nihilism, existential depression and despair.

BECOMING ATTUNED TO SUBTLE ENERGIES

Healing with colour is based upon understanding these principles. Traditionally those who did so were seers or clairvoyants, mystics who could perceive subtle energies, and thus the colours of the human energy field, directly.

Contemporary clairvoyants believe that others can also learn to perceive these energies. Those who cannot 'see' the colours of the human energy field objectively can become attuned to vibrations of colour. This sensitivity may be latent in all of us, and is reflected in commonplace descriptions of people as 'in a black mood', 'green with envy', 'in the pink' or 'blue'; and as giving out good or bad 'vibes'. Most people can develop heightened sensitivity to these vibrations quite easily.

Just as blindfolded subjects can distinguish colours by 'feel' (see Chapter One), so people can detect various physical sensations in their hands and fingertips when they pass their hands through the energy field of another person some two to three inches above the surface of the body. Heat and cold, tingling, pins and needles, pulsing, pressure or electric shock provide reliable information about pain and other symptoms of disease which can be checked by talking to the person.

THE ART OF DOWSING

An ages-old technique for detecting subtle energies is dowsing. The amount and direction of the energy flowing through a chakra can be detected using a pendulum. After a few seconds the pendulum will usually begin to move. Its movement may be circular, elliptical or from side to side; and smooth or erratic. The direction and radius of the movement show the amount and direction of the energy flowing through the chakra. The radius of the movement is related both to the strength and quantity of the energy flowing through the chakra and the energy of the dowser. The wider the radius the greater the energy flow. The speed of the movement indicates the rate of energy flow through the chakra. Very fast movement suggests that the chakra is being overworked, whereas a slow speed means that the energy flow through the chakra is sluggish.

Clockwise movement of the pendulum indicates an open chakra that is functioning effectively; the feelings and processes governed by it are therefore balanced and healthy. Counter-clockwise movement indicates that the chakra is closed or blocked so that energy cannot flow through it. The result is that the feelings and functions governed by it are not balanced and are probably experienced negatively by the person.

Between these two extremes various other movements may be described by the pendulum. An elliptical swing indicates a left/right imbalance of the energy flow in the body, and that one side of the body is stronger than the other. The more the circular movement of the pendulum is distorted above any given chakra the more severe is the energy distortion. A severe right/left split is suggested by a back and forth movement of the pendulum at a 45-degree angle to the vertical axis of the body; the larger the pendulum movement the greater the amount of energy contained in the distortion. Back and forth movements of the pendulum parallel to the body's vertical axis or perpendicular to it also indicate energy distortion. In the former the energy is being diverted upwards and in the latter downwards, suggesting that it is expressed inappropriately through a higher chakra, or suppressed. Chaotic movement means that there is considerable flux in the chakra and in its functioning. When the pendulum exhibits no movement at all the chakra is no longer functioning and is not metabolising energy from the universal energy field. This is an unhealthy state and if maintained over time, the person will become ill.

APPLIED KINESIOLOGY

Another form of diagnosis used in healing with colour is
applied kinesiology. This works on a similar basis to
dowsing in that it relies on imperceptible muscular
responses to subtle energies to establish imbalances in the
body's energy system. The healer holds a colour at eye
level with the left arm while extending the right arm
horizontally. As each colour is perceived, he or she applies
gentle downwards pressure to the extended right arm.
Lack of resistance to this pressure suggests that the person
needs the colour he or she is perceiving.

SPINAL DIAGNOSIS

A more complex form of diagnosis, developed by Theo
Gimbel, involves dowsing the spine with the fingers. This
is based on a similar principle to radionics, and involves a
specimen taken from the person which is referred to as a
'witness'. In radionics this is usually something from the
body, such as a spot of blood or lock of hair, but in
Gimbel's method a signature or photograph of the subject
may be used. This is placed under a chart depicting the
spine. The therapist then moves the middle finger of his or
her dominant hand above the chart vertebra by vertebra,
feeling the sensations that arise. Vertebrae considered
'inactive' produce no sensations, while active ones produce
hot, cold, repelling of or tingling in the finger. This form
of diagnosis is based on the idea that the subtle energy
along the spinal channel is organised in sections associated
with different physical and psychological functions. Each
section comprises eight vertebrae, associated with colours
in rainbow sequence. Diagnosis of mental and physical
conditions is determined by which vertebrae — and hence
which colours — are active or inactive in any section.

Gimbel's rationale is that when white light is passed through each of four carefully placed prisms, eight coloured beams emerge, including magenta. He claims this is clearly visible on white paper printed with lines and bars, and results from the juxtaposition of black and white, which mixes red with ultraviolet light. The addition of this extra colour produces four pairs of complementary colours when these are presented in a rainbow sequence as a colour wheel. These complementary pairs are red and turquoise, orange and blue, yellow and violet, green and magenta. In combination with each other they produce white light. Gimbel stresses that complementary pairs of colours should always be used together in treatment using light, in order to achieve the balance of energy essential for good health. He maintains that if a colour used in treatment is not balanced by its complementary colour, the condition may be made worse. Many modern colour therapists trained by Gimbel believe that there are eight colours in the spectrum, and have introduced a major chakra between the throat and heart to accommodate it. In so doing they are not only departing from the traditional chakra system and practice in healing with colour, but also from the accepted laws of physics.

METHODS OF HEALING WITH COLOUR
COLOURED LIGHT

This has been used in healing throughout history in combination with shapes, sounds, minerals, flowers, foods and other forms with the same characteristic vibrational frequency. Coloured light can be projected on to various parts of the body using various devices, including lamps and filters. In many instances the light provided is defined in shapes believed to enhance the colour's energetic effect.

Contemporary colour therapists use full-spectrum lamps
fitted with special quartz filters that can produce colours
of all wavelengths and frequencies. This cannot be achieved
with ordinary artificial lights, because they emit some
wavelengths more powerfully than others. The spectrum of
light emitted from a fluorescent tube, for example, is
weaker in reds than blue, green and ultraviolet.

Treatment using properly filtered full-spectrum light is
powerful. Selecting the wrong colour and/or exposure
time may create imbalances in the body's energies, so
coloured light should be used for healing only under the
guidance of a trained practitioner. However, full-spectrum
lights which produce all the wavelengths of colour can be
purchased and used safely and beneficially by people who
spend much of their time exposed to artificial light.
Indirect use of coloured light may also be beneficial. In
India the traditional practice of drinking water which has
been exposed to sunlight through various coloured glasses
is still prescribed in the treatment of specific conditions.
Many colour therapists use similar elixirs, developed by
Edwin Babbit. These preparations can be made and used at
home quite safely. While use of the wrong colours will not
confer any benefit on the user, they will not do any harm.

COLOURED PIGMENTS

In the form of dyes and paints, coloured pigments have
been widely used in healing since the earliest times. These
have different properties from coloured light. The primary
colours of pigments — red, yellow and blue — cannot be
created by mixing any other colours. A mixture of these
primaries looks black, because together they absorb all the
light that falls on them. A red pigment absorbs all the
wavelengths from light except red, which it reflects; a

yellow pigment absorbs everything except yellow; and a blue pigment absorbs everything but blue. When a pair of pigment primaries are mixed together they produce secondaries; red and yellow make orange, red and blue make violet, and yellow and blue make green, producing the seven principal colours traditionally associated with the colour spectrum.

The general principles followed by colour therapists are that energies can be stimulated by encouraging everyday exposure to certain colours. This can be through clothes and accessories or in the decoration and furnishing of your living and working environments, and by eating certain foods. The principle of resonance is used to determine which energies are expressed most by an individual. A person who usually wears a lot of red is assumed to be resonating with that vibration, and so may benefit from adding other colours, notably the 'cooler' calming shades of green and blue, if she tends to become 'overheated' or overexcited or suffer from ailments associated with an excess of red energy. By contrast, someone who suffers from not having enough of this energy and avoids wearing the colour may benefit from doing so, and from being in red surroundings. Such a person may also benefit from eating red meat, and food such as beets, radishes, tomatoes, red-skinned fruits and spices such as cayenne, cloves and capsicum pepper. These should be avoided by those with an excess of red energy.

This awareness forms the basis of Ayurveda, the traditional medicine of the Indian sub-continent, and one of the oldest systems of healing in the world. Similar principles are also fundamental to traditional Chinese medicine.

GEMSTONES AND CRYSTALS

These are widely used to augment colour on and around the body, and may be worn as talismans, amulets and jewellery, placed over the chakras or in the energy field of the body. In treatment they are used with minerals and metals. Gemstones and crystals ground or powdered into water have for many many years been prescribed as oral medication in Ayurveda. However, it has long been understood that the healing properties of gems are transferred to water or another liquid in which the stone is immersed, and gem elixirs have been used in healing since ancient times. They are prepared by potentising water containing gemstones by exposure to natural light, and taken by mouth. When applied externally they can be combined with creams and essential oils and used in massage, and also added to baths. Gems may also be placed in baths with the appropriate elixir.

ESSENTIAL OILS

Derived from flowering plants to augment the effects of colour in healing, the use of essential oils is also an ancient practice. Today an increasing number of people combine colour and aromatherapy in healing.

Colour is often the link between essential oils and the chakras. Patricia Davis identifies essential oils traditionally classed as Base Notes in perfumery and reddish in colour as resonating with the base chakra. Hence Myrrh may have an energising effect when base chakra energy is low. Davis suggests that Bergamot and Inula, both green oils, connect with the heart chakra. With Melissa, an oil with a 'green' aroma, Bergamot and Inula may be valuable where there is an energy blockage between the second and third chakras.

Two oils are identified by Davis as particularly appropriate to the throat chakra — German blue Camomile and the paler blue English Camomile; Juniper, whose indigo berries correspond with the brow chakra, and Lavender with the crown chakra. These oils may be applied by way of massage, baths, inhalers or burners, or simply by putting a couple of drops on handkerchiefs, pillows and the like.

Inger Naess of Norway has developed a line of colour oils for use in baths under the trade name Colour Bath. These are pure essential oils to balance chakra energies. They can be used to increase or reduce certain energies; a person with a lot of red energy should tone down this energy by taking a green bath, whereas someone needing red energy should take a red bath.

FLOWER ESSENCES

Gem elixirs are often used with flower essences, with which they are believed to have a synergistic effect. These are produced in much the same way as elixirs, by potentising water containing flowers in full sunlight, and used in similar ways.

The colour of the plant from which the essences are derived is perhaps less important than the 'colour' associated with its vibration.

Edward Bach, the physician who was the first person in modern times to develop a system of healing with flower essences, organised his flower remedies into seven groups, each associated with a different colour and shown accordingly on a colour wheel chart still produced by the Bach Centre in England. The energy imbalances treated by the remedies in each of these groups broadly corresponds with the function of the chakras. Although Bach made no reference to chakras or colour in developing his system, it is nevertheless probable that colour is a reliable guide to their selection and use.

PSYCHOLOGICAL METHODS OF HEALING WITH COLOUR

The methods of diagnosis and treatment described above basically rely on physical sensitivity. However, traditional methods of diagnosis and treatment depend more on psychological sensitivity, and therefore on intuition and insight — literally inner sensing, or seeing. The ancients recognised that mental images are energy forms with numerous applications in healing, and may involve any of the senses or a combination of them. It is not the case, as is often assumed, that images are necessarily visual. An image involves not merely 'seeing' a picture in the mind's eye but sensing or experiencing it in various ways. As Brennan writes, 'Perceiving means receiving. Perception is receiving what is already there.'

Much of what 'is there' in life, though, is difficult to grasp because it cannot easily be conceived or conveyed verbally. Images allow many non-verbal phenomena such as physical, emotional and spiritual experiences to be represented in the mind. They therefore provide a way of thinking about what was formerly 'unthinkable'. As such, they facilitate conscious awareness of much that is ordinarily unconscious, and so they can be used not only to develop awareness of the effects of subtle energies and colour, but also to provide reliable information about these phenomena. Buddhist traditions emphasise the importance of identifying with the chakras by focusing awareness on them, and thus sensing rather than thinking about them. Colour images produced in this way are used diagnostically in various approaches to healing with colour. (See Part Two.)

VISUALISATION

Forming images in the mind's eye, or visualisation, is widely used in healing with colour. As Brennan points out, this has an entirely different function:

> The process of visualisation is actively creating. In visualisation you create a picture in your mind and give it energy. If you continue to hold it clearly in your mind and give it energy, you can eventually create it in your life. You have thus given it form and substance. The clearer the image and the more emotional energy you project into it, the more you will be able to create it in your life.

Contemporary research on imagery lends support to this view. Much has been written over the past twenty years which confirms that images are indeed a powerful force, and can have profound physical and psychological effects. According to Dr Larry Dossey, these effects are as potent as those produced by any drug, and so imagery should be regarded as medicine in the truest sense of the word.

It is now known that imagining something is essentially the same as perceiving it in the external world. Simply imagining sucking a lemon, for example, has a direct effect on the salivary glands. The effects of imagery on heart rate, blood pressure, blood flow, electrodermal activity and immune response have all been confirmed in experiments.

This principle underpins various practices used in healing with colour, notably colour visualisation and meditating on coloured images. By imagining colour you produce vibrations of a certain frequency, which when

directed to the energy centres of the body can produce
various psychological and physical effects. Visualisation of
and meditation on colour are also thought to strengthen
its energies and increase its healing properties. Meditation
on coloured light, pigment, crystals, gemstones, minerals,
elixirs, flowers and foods used in healing is believed to
reinforce their effects. In traditional Indian and Chinese
medicine, visualising light being drawn into the body in
various ways is recommended for self-healing.

Visualisation of light and colour also plays a large part
in Tibetan medicine. Brilliant white or coloured light is
imagined radiating from a deity and flowing through your
being, purifying it mentally and physically. This light can
be directed by you to a diseased area of the body, or
outwards into the universe to heal others. In Chinese
medicine, people are encouraged to enhance, redirect and
normalise vital energies by imagining them in various
ways. A common breathing exercise is to imagine
breathing in coloured light. This is also practised in many
other traditions, ancient and modern, together with other
kinds of colour imagery.

The practice of channelling or sending colour to
vitalise someone else's depleted energies is common in
healing with colour. This involves visualising a colour and
imagining 'sending' it to the person to be treated. In this
way colour may be channelled through the hands directly
into the body of a person, or it may be sent to a person at
some distance through the universal energy field.

Healers often use coloured crystals as wands to direct
subtle energy into the chakras, and at Hygeia Studios,
England, a hand-held torch that focuses light through a
stained glass filter and a clear quartz crystal, has been
developed for the same purpose.

So images can be used both in sensing and sending energies, and these functions are combined in many different ancient and modern approaches to healing with colour. These two processes are fundamental to Therapeutic Touch, developed by Dolores Krieger, former Professor of Nursing at New York University. Therapeutic Touch is now regarded in the USA and Canada — and increasingly in Britain — as a natural extension of professional nursing skills.

Training in Therapeutic Touch takes place in five stages. First, the healer must learn to relax and focus her attention inwards so to achieve a meditative state. Next, she makes an assessment of the patient's energies by passing her hands through the energy field surrounding the body some two to three inches above its surface.

Differences in energy flow resulting from imbalance are detected through sensations in the healer's hands, such as variations in temperature, pins and needles, tingling, pulsing, pressure or electric shock and associated colour imagery. The healer then relieves congestion by stroking or sweeping gestures away from the affected part, and after washing or shaking her hands to remove the charge picked up from the patient, places her hands on either side of the affected area and imagines directing energy into it. The energy is modulated through use of colour imagery, so the healer mentally pictures sending blue energy to cool or sedate, red to warm or stimulate, yellow to energise, and continues to do so until the patient's body feels balanced.

In Part Two you are invited to combine these techniques of sensing and sending colour energy by way of imagery, and so discover and develop your true colours as a means for healing yourself and others.

PART TWO

Discovering Your True Colours

CHAPTER THREE

Developing Colour Consciousness

Implicit in healing with colour is the ideal of perfect
health as symbolised by a rainbow. Like a rainbow, a
healthy person should distribute all energies,
wavelengths and colours in a balanced way. The aim of
healing with colour is to attune the person to their
rainbow, to vitalise the chakras and exhort them to a
healthy level. It is therefore concerned with increasing
awareness of colour, its subtle effects and influences on life,
and with the development of what might be called colour
consciousness.

The first step in developing colour consciousness is to
identify the colours that figure in your life, and the
experiences you associate with them. You can begin by
answering the following questions:

What colours are you wearing now?
Why did you choose to wear these clothes?
How do you feel when wearing them?
How do these colours compare with those you normally
wear?
What is your favourite colour?
What is your least favourite colour?
When you look into your wardrobe, what colours do you
see?

Is there more of any colour or colours than others?

What colours are missing or not well represented there?

What colour or colours would you never wear and why?

Are there any colours that you would like to wear but
   cannot or do not wear? What are your reasons for not
   doing so?

How frequently can you not find anything to wear that
   you feel comfortable in?

What colours predominate in your main living areas?

What colours predominate in your work space?

What colour is your bedroom?

What colour is your car and its interior upholstery?

The significance of your answers lies in the fact that a person's energies express themselves through colour. The principle underlying this idea is that of resonance. Energies that naturally vibrate at certain frequencies are excited by energies in the environment vibrating at precisely the same frequency. These energies 'strike a chord', quite literally. If you pluck the E string of a violin, for example, the E string of a nearby violin will begin to vibrate in harmony, because both strings are tuned and responsive to a particular frequency.

In the same way, certain colours strike a chord with us when their vibrations match our own. We are likely to prefer these to colours whose vibrations we do not resonate with, just as we tend to like people we consider to be on the same wavelength as ourselves and to dislike those we don't get on with. Our dislike of certain colours suggests that we are not resonating with them, and thus not functioning effectively in respect of these frequencies. So colour preference is an indication of the subtle energies we are attuned to.

Even though we express liking for them we may avoid certain colours. How often have you heard someone say that they like a colour but don't wear it or live with it because it is 'too much' or 'a little over the top'? This suggests that she doesn't want to excite these particular frequencies, maybe because she is over-energised in that area, probably because it is compensating for energies that are not being properly used elsewhere. So when a colour is avoided, either because these energies are not being used or because they are being over-used, the colour preference shows the need to balance these energies.

The quantity of energy used by a person is as important as its quality, and some idea of this can be gained from the intensity of colour preferred. Many women express a preference for pastel or dilute shades, and tend to tone down bright or strong colours. Some of those who like bright colours don't wear them because they don't want to draw attention to themselves. By doing so, they are reflecting social conventions regarding the expression of gender-appropriate energies. Can it be coincidental that the colour pink, traditionally associated with women in western culture, has calming effects and suppresses the expression of anger and aggression? Or that blue, traditionally associated with baby boys in our culture, is the colour of self-expression? Women often choose to wear navy blue to work, and especially for job interviews and business meetings with men, again very probably because this colour has a subduing effect and expresses control.

Perhaps even more alarming is the number of women who avoid wearing colours they enjoy wearing because they have been told by others that they don't suit them. These may be colour counsellors who base their judgments on hair or eye colour and skin tone, rather than on the balanced expression of personal energies. Once again this highlights the impact of social constraints on self-expression. Men, however, often express a preference for shades of blue, which is consistent with social conditioning and expectations. Many men also wear more muddy colours that women often describe as 'mucky'. Khaki colours may not so much camouflage the individual, but show clearly that hearty green energies are dysfunctional, just as earthy shades may suggest that basic physical and creative energies are not being properly expressed. Men in grey have almost become an emblem of our times — both a depressing thought and a depressing colour.

Many women state emphatically that they would never wear yellow or orange, colours associated with intellect, will-power and strong passions, again reflecting stereotypical views on the energies it is appropriate for women in our culture to suppress. Although there may be fewer strictures about men appearing 'bright' and energetic, they tend not to wear these clothes in the workplace and confine them to leisure wear, or ties. Purple is avoided equally by men and women, suggesting the lack of a spiritual dimension in their lives.

Generally, few people wear or even possess a full range of coloured clothes. The garments they wear tend to reflect one or other end of the colour spectrum, or its mid-range. Some possess clothes of all but one colour. A small minority of people wear only one colour. Even those who possess a wide range of colours may wear some of these more than others. This may reflect other social conventions such as fashion, or more idiosyncratic factors like physical state and mood.

If you find that you wear only a limited range of colours, identify those you rarely or never wear, and consult the details in Chapter Two about the appropriate chakra. Remember that red is associated with the base chakra, orange with the second chakra, yellow with the third chakra, green with the fourth, blue with the fifth, dark blue or indigo with the sixth, and purple or violet with the crown chakra. In this way you should be able to identify the energies these colours relate to, and their implications for your psychological and physical well-being.

A COLOUR DIARY

You can develop awareness of the effects of colour on your physical state, moods, feelings, attitudes, interests, activities and relationships by keeping a colour diary. Try this first for one week. Every day record what colours and colour combinations you wear while doing various things, and note how you feel physically, mentally, emotionally and spiritually as you do so. This sounds easier than it is. You may change your clothes several times a day, usually without thinking about it. Keeping a diary of this kind requires you to become aware of those changes, when and where they occur, and their effects on a number of different personal levels.

You may find that the colours lacking in your clothes are also absent from your living and working environment, or that you wear certain colours to compensate for lack of colour in these settings. Try keeping a diary for a second week, adding your feelings about your usual surroundings and your reactions to decor, lighting and such like. You may identify with Jackie, who was initially delighted to be able to save money on the furnishings of her new house, which was decorated and carpeted throughout in shades of grey.

After four weeks she found that she couldn't stay in the house for any length of time without becoming depressed, and when her husband commented that she always seemed to be going out she insisted that they redecorate despite the cost. Jackie decorated the living room in shades of pink and green which she, her family and friends found very relaxing. She also painted her older daughter's bedroom pink, but in an attempt to brighten the bedroom of her three-year-old daughter, painted it bright yellow. Some time later she realised that the child had never slept one complete night in this room, whereas she would sleep throughout the night in her sister's room.

Lyn changed the 'girly' pink shades of her bedroom when she married and her husband moved into her house. She subsequently attributed the cooling and eventual breakdown of their relationship to the blue/grey shades she chose instead.

Graham, who felt 'chilled out' by the pale blue decor of his friend's living room, insisted on changing the blues chosen as bedroom decoration by his wife to pink, which he felt was warmer and softer. Gerry, a physical education teacher, found his school's grey sports hall totally depressing, an observation shared by other teachers obliged to invigilate examinations in there. The school inspectors agreed, and suggested that a brighter colour might improve both sporting and scholastic performance.

By contrast, the managers of a company whose workers tended to congregate and chat in the men's toilets, solved the problem by painting the walls bright orange. As a result it was no longer a 'rest room', and the workers hastily returned to their workshops. Carl, the director of an art gallery, was puzzled as to why an interactive multi-media exhibition designed for three- to five-year-olds failed to excite them. His staff, who had anticipated having to deal with chaos as up to sixty children played with spectacular computer generated games, were astonished to find that the children instead seemed restrained and sombre. It transpired that no one at the gallery had given much thought to the overall colour of the display, and the lighting. The walls, furniture and fittings were predominantly dark blue, lit by subdued fluorescent lighting which is low in red, orange and yellow wavelengths, and distorts colours, making them seem more blue. This created a subdued environment almost totally lacking in the reds, oranges and yellows needed to stimulate and excite children of this age.

By keeping a detailed diary you may be able to identify those colours you resonate with and that are comfortable for you. You may then wish to experiment with colours you don't normally wear or expose yourself to. Pam found that when wearing brown, a colour she often wore teamed with fashionable creams, taupes and beige, she tended to withdraw mentally and emotionally. By experimenting as suggested, first with turquoise earrings and necklaces, then with scarves and eventually with sweaters and dresses, she found that she could speak up for herself more and that her normally hushed voice gained timbre. As a result of being more confident about expressing herself Pam went on to try purples, violets, magenta and pinks and was astonished not only to feel more vibrant but also to find others telling her she looked years younger.

Similarly, Ann, who hadn't worn green for years, began to experiment with it, initially by walking in the countryside and then by wearing a green scarf. She soon found that she was emotionally calmer and more relaxed. As she brought more and more green into her life she realised that she had healed a heart 'broken' some years before by the death of a loved one.

Experimenting with colour and observing its effects is not a matter of thinking of colour, but experiencing it. As Barbara Ann Brennan points out, in energetic terms thought is a yellow vibration, so irrespective of what colour you think of, you will create yellow. So you need to experiment with what it is like to 'be' in a state of blue. This involves being aware of how you feel when you wear blue or sit in a blue light, and of what blue means to you — how it looks, feels and sounds. In order to develop colour consciousness you need to explore your relationship to every colour in this way. The exercises in the chapters that follow will help you to do so.

CHAPTER FOUR

Relaxing with Colour

If asked 'How do you relax?' what would your response
be? Would you say you watch TV, read books, complete
crossword puzzles, go for walks, engage in sports or have
a few drinks with friends? Whatever your answer, you are
unlikely to say that you 'cease to maintain the tension in
the muscles of your body'. Yet this is precisely how we
relax. Generally, when people think they are relaxed they
are not. They may remain mentally active, physically
aroused, anxious, fidgety, restless and react to the slightest
noise. Their blood pressure may be raised and their pulse
rate increased. They may breathe irregularly, swallow
frequently, show involuntary reflexes such as wrinkling of
the forehead, and stiffness in the muscles of the face, all of
which indicate residual tension.

In true relaxation, tension is absent, breathing is
regular, there is no reflex swallowing, pulse rate and blood
pressure decrease, and you sit or lie quietly with flaccid
limbs and motionless eyelids. Less obviously but more
importantly, the mental processes that generate bodily
tension in the first place are switched off — the habitual
thoughts, concerns, preoccupations and anxieties. The
mind is therefore blank in the sense that the 'sound' has
been turned down, but it is not empty. Images present
themselves fleetingly. Just as television transforms
electromagnetic energies into sights and sounds, so your
mind transforms subtle energies into various sensory
images. It is no more true to say that these images are
produced because the sound is off than it is to say that
turning the sound down produces pictures on a television
screen. They have been there all along, but have been

unattended to. Similarly, many people 'watch' TV mainly
by listening to the soundtrack and pay little attention to
the images on the screen. When the sound is turned down
they are obliged to look at these images to find out what
is going on.

In much the same way, most people need to turn
down the sound — the chatter of verbal thought which
acts as a constant soundtrack accompanying everything
that goes on in and around them — before they can
receive the images produced by their own mind. This
occurs spontaneously during sleep and at other times
when the mind wanders from its usual preoccupations.
However, although dreams, daydreams and fantasies can
provide a great deal of information about the self, they
tend to be dismissed as fanciful. Relaxation enables us to
focus attention on the images we receive so we can
understand their meaning and the information they
convey about aspects of ourselves of which ordinarily we
are unaware.

If you have begun to notice some of the effects of
colour in your life you may want to develop your
awareness further. The following exercise, which combines
relaxation and imagery, will help you to do this. It can be
repeated as often as you like, because it reflects the
energies that are being expressed at any time and will
change as you and the circumstances of your life alter
(although certain features may remain constant). Awareness
of both variable and constant features will give you greater
insight into how effectively you are using your energies,
enabling you to monitor and balance them. I recommend
that you take your time, and allow twenty minutes for the
exercise. It is a good idea to record the instructions on
cassette, or to ask someone to read them to you until you
are familiar enough with the steps to do without such help.

EXERCISE 1

SEEING YOUR TRUE COLOURS

Find somewhere quiet and make yourself comfortable, either sitting or lying (preferably the former so you don't go to sleep).

Having done this, become aware of your surroundings and how you feel. Then close your eyes (if this is not possible because of any physical problems, or difficult because of contact lenses, focus on a fixed point or object within your line of vision, such as a mark on a wall, ceiling or floor).

Now gradually withdraw your attention from your surroundings, and bring it to the boundary between your body and adjacent surfaces. As you do so, notice whether the contact is uncomfortable or painful, and adjust your position to make yourself as comfortable as possible. You may find that you need to remove restrictive clothing, shoes, jewellery or glasses. At any point in the exercise when you feel the need to, adjust your position to reduce pain or discomfort.

When you are positioned comfortably, turn your attention to your feelings. How *do* you feel? Do you feel silly or guilty about taking time to do the exercise, reluctant or impatient to get on with it?

How self-conscious are you? Are you worried about being seen by others, or that they are nearby? Are you worried that you might not be able to 'do' the exercise, or what you might discover about yourself if you can? Your reactions may reflect some of the basic anxieties of your life. If during any part of the exercise thoughts, feelings, memories or impressions come to mind, make a mental note of them as they may be significant.

Now bring your attention to your toes and tighten

them as much as you can. Keep doing this until you can identify the extent of its effects throughout your body and then let go, observing as you do so the difference between the sensations of tightening and letting go. Pause for a moment as you focus awareness on your toes, before repeating this action two or three times. Then, progressing slowly upwards from your toes, repeat this process, tightening and letting go in turn your legs, knees, thighs, buttocks, lower back, stomach, chest, shoulders, both arms and hands, your neck, brow, eyes, nose, lips, mouth and jaw.

Then bring your attention back to your toes, and starting with them tighten successively all the other parts of your body so that it is tense throughout its length. Increase this tightness as much as you can, and hold it for several moments before letting go. Allow the resulting sensation of floppiness to spread throughout your body. Then repeat this action twice more. Your body should now be fully relaxed, with your jaw slack and your mouth open. If they are not, repeat the action, accentuating the tightness in your jaw and letting your mouth fall open when you relax.

Having done so, breathe in through your nose and out through your open mouth, observing how this feels and its effects on your body. Still breathing in this way, spend a few moments becoming aware of the sensations throughout your body. If relaxed, your limbs and body should feel heavy and warm. Scan your body from top to bottom, noting any tightness, discomfort or pain that persists despite these attempts.

Now focus your attention on your chest and observe your breathing. Is it regular or irregular; shallow or deep; difficult or easy?

Still focusing on your chest, imagine that there is a butterfly resting there and that as you breathe in and out it gradually spreads its wings to their full extent as though you are breathing energy and life into it. Look at it carefully, noting its size and colour and your feelings towards it. When the butterfly's wings are fully extended and it seems prepared to fly off, breathe out deeply and watch it fly away. Be aware of your thoughts and feelings as it does so. Then imagine that you follow it, noting all the sensations you experience.

After a while it comes to a rest, and as you do likewise, you find yourself in a pleasant situation where you feel relaxed, comfortable and secure. Every detail of this place becomes vivid as you pay careful attention to the sights, sounds, smells and sensations there. When you realise that you can be really yourself there, begin to pay particular attention to colour and allow yourself to experience it fully. As you do so, take note of how you feel, and any features of the 'real' you that seem particularly significant.

Don't try to direct your thoughts to create specific images, and don't censor them. Simply allow images to emerge spontaneously — receive them as they arise. Also be aware of any difficulty you have in imagining yourself in such a place; and of any distracting thoughts, feelings, memories or sensations that arise. Don't dwell on these, but don't try to suppress them. Merely make a mental note and allow them to disappear.

Having entered into this experience as fully as you can, ask yourself what its significance might be and what the different colours you have seen may represent. When you have answered these questions as best you can, allow the image to fade and return to ordinary awareness by opening your eyes.

Try recording your experience on cassette or in a written log so that you can reflect upon it and refer to it later. Doing so will help you to cross-reference and interrelate it with experiences from later exercises. The following commentary may also help you to understand the personal significance of your imagery more fully. If you feel you may be influenced by knowing others' responses, don't read the commentary until you have completed and recorded the exercise.

COMMENTARY

The butterfly image used in the above exercise is a very potent symbol of the self. The ancient Greeks used the term *psyche* to refer to both the butterfly and the self or soul — the spiritual nature of the individual. Universally, the butterfly represents spiritual qualities, transformation, metamorphosis, change and freedom. Paying attention to this image invariably reveals important personal issues.

From the responses of large numbers of people, it seems clear that the colours of the butterfly reflect the energies that they are expressing currently, whereas the colours of the place the butterfly leads them to represent the energies they need to express in order to be really themselves. The image focuses awareness on personal authenticity; that is, on how much of the true self is suppressed in order to conform with social pressures and expectations — and what might be expressed if the person were to show their true colours.

Butterflies naturally occur in all colours and colour combinations, but this is not reflected in response to the above exercise. Typically, solid red, orange, brown or pink butterflies don't appear, whereas those that are wholly yellow, green, blue, turquoise, purple, and white are often described. All-black butterflies are described only rarely, and wholly brown butterflies are very uncommon. White reflects all colours, and suggests healthy functioning, where all energies are being used and expressed in a balanced way.

The deeper the colour imagined the more intensely the colour energies represented by the butterfly are being expressed at the present time. When the colour is bright this energy may predominate over all other energies and need balancing accordingly. Bright yellow butterflies may therefore be imagined by headstrong people who intellectualise everything and whose mental attitude colours everything including sex, feelings and self-expression. Such rational people speak from the head rather than the heart, and may be quite out of touch with their feelings. Typically, one woman who imagined a huge bright yellow butterfly reported feeling envious because she couldn't identify with it.

People who imagine bright green butterflies may allow their emotions to colour everything, whereas those who imagine blue butterflies may be rather selfish, seeing everything in terms of how it affects and reflects on themselves. Bright purple butterflies often indicate individuals whose spiritual concerns predominate, sometimes with the result that they are out of touch with ordinary reality.

Dilute colours appear to be associated with energies and potential not being adequately used or expressed. In some cases this is extreme. Transparent butterflies suggest no sense of presence. One woman who imagined a very pale butterfly saw this as accurately reflecting the fact that she did not express anything of her true self.

More usually colour is evident, but pale. Pale yellow, green and blue butterflies are often imagined. Sometimes these colours are described as washed out, which suggests that this energy has been drained. In relation to green energies this shows that the emotional energies have been overworked, which has implications for immune functioning. (The relationship between emotional trauma and immune-related diseases such as cancers is in fact well-established.)

'Drained' yellow energies suggest that intellectual and work-related demands may be taking their toll, and that the person is susceptible to stress and related physical and psychological problems. Washed out blue energies are likely to indicate poor self-expression and a tendency to throat and speech disorders.

When white butterflies are tinged with other colours, fringed or tipped with colour or have spots or patches of colour, this suggests that these energies are somewhat out of balance, to the extent indicated by the intensity of the colours. A woman who imagined a white butterfly with pale yellow spots had little confidence in her intellectual ability, and didn't express her views in case she revealed her shortcomings.

Orange and white butterflies are quite often imagined, and indicate that physical energies need regulating. Pale orange suggests that the person is lacking in energy and vitality. Bright orange, on the other hand, tends to characterise people who are highly energetic and constantly on the go, such as Jan, whose excessive energy was represented in numerous vivid orange spots on an otherwise white butterfly, shown in her hyperactivity and inability to relax.

The size of the butterfly appears to reflect the potential energy available to the individual. Its behaviour and the person's attitudes towards it are also significant.

Large butterflies suggest considerable potential, which is, however, often under-used. People may attempt to restrain the butterfly because they fear losing it, and flatten it in the attempt. One man reported holding his butterfly 'close to his chest' so that its true colours couldn't be seen. Many butterflies are extremely delicate and fragile. Some flutter their wings but are unable to stretch them fully or fly. Some crumple horribly at the first attempt, while others remain with wings outstretched but are still unable to fly. Others flutter their wings and make gestures towards flying without actually doing so.

A number of butterflies are imagined as tattoos, silhouettes, templates, appliqué decorations, origami or cardboard cut-outs. So although they may be colourful, they are not alive. These images indicate the extent to which individuals may stifle or restrict expression of their potential, or crumple in the face of their own reality.

Whatever their shape or substance, butterflies usually combine several colours. Where one colour is tinged with black this suggests that a trace of negativity runs throughout the expression of this energy and that it is not being fully realised. Wings that are black tipped or fringed may indicate that negativity interferes with the full expression of these energies. Red fringed with black is suggestive of insecurity and poor self-confidence, especially in relation to the body and sexuality. Orange tipped with black is suggestive of negative reactions, the tendency to doubt your gut feelings, and feelings of powerlessness.

Yellow tipped with black may suggest negative thoughts and attitudes; and green tipped with black may signify emotions such as resentment and jealousy, and difficulties in relationships. Blue tipped with black may

indicate coolness, distance, aloofness; and purple tipped
with black may be associated with feelings of dread,
despair, hopelessness and lack of purpose.

Black spots, splashes, blobs or patches suggest
negativity or a more intermittent failure fully to express
energies. These may be thought of as blemishes on the
individual's character — not in a critical way, but inasmuch
as they represent potential whose expression is patchy in
quality, occurrence and intensity.

One woman who imagined a large, deep green, exotic
butterfly whose secondary wings were banded and barred
with black, saw this as reflecting very strong emotions that
were sometimes not fully or appropriately expressed.
Indeed she felt so strongly about some issues that she
couldn't allow herself to acknowledge fully much less
express these feelings.

A person's imagery may combine several of the above
features. One woman was alarmed by the size of her
imagined butterfly, which spread very wide across her
chest. Every time it attempted to fly off she tried to catch
it, until finally it crumpled completely. Afterwards she
acknowledged always having had difficulty holding onto
anything in life, and losing what she wanted by trying too
hard. She recognised that the colour of her butterfly —
pale mauve edged with black — was significant, as was the
fact that she was dressed in the same colour. The woman
associated purple with mourning and with the sadness of
being a loser, and realised that mauve, a dilute purple,
represented her attempt to conceal this sadness from others
so as to be acceptable to them. Only the black edges of
the butterfly's wings revealed her true feelings.

This woman interpreted the significance of the
colours in her imagery with no prior knowledge or

understanding of their traditional meanings. From the traditional perspective, purple is associated with spiritual issues such as purpose in life, with transcendence, joy and ecstatic experience.

The butterflies imagined by many people combine several colours. Some liken theirs to a Red Admiral, a common British butterfly which is predominantly red, orange and brown with some areas of black. Its colours are associated with the lower chakra energies and functions. Where brown appears in imagery it indicates stagnant energy. Muddy reds may suggest lack of sexual fulfilment or creativity, and brown juxtaposed with red that expression of this basic energy alternates — sometimes quite intense, at other times blocked. In conjunction with orange it suggests lack of emotional vitality, sluggishness and feelings of powerlessness.

Deborah hadn't seen much significance in her 'Red Admiral' until she related its colours to these features. She then admitted to deep-seated insecurities and lack of confidence, which had resulted in emotional difficulties and body image problems. By her thirties, having been both anorexic and bulimic, she had become obese, and she admitted to wearing dark colours to hide her weight. Deborah also had difficulty expressing herself, and as a result she had fared badly at interviews and was unfulfilled in her job.

Following the exercise, where she imagined following the Red Admiral to a tropical paradise of blue skies, lush green vegetation and vivid red, orange and yellow flowers, she decided to wear these colours. Deborah was subsequently delighted not only to find her confidence greatly increased but also, following an interview, to be offered a job in which she felt she could show her true colours.

As Deborah's imagery reveals, clues to how the energies represented by the butterfly can be balanced are provided by the situation it leads the individual to. One woman identified strongly with the huge, turquoise-blue butterfly she imagined. Like her, it was a high flyer, and she was initially happy to follow it up into the sky; but the higher it flew, the more uncomfortable she became. She began to feel vulnerable, and concerned that the butterfly would be 'shot down'. She felt that to go higher would not be 'right' for her and was therefore greatly relieved when suddenly it led her to an Amazon rain forest that was predominantly bright green but full of flowers of all colours. She took this as a sign of the anxiety she felt as a high-flying professional without any real sense of direction in her life.

Taken together, the butterfly and the place it leads you to present a full spectrum of colours, which represent everyone's true colours and the healthy expression of their full range of energies or potential.

CHAPTER FIVE

Identifying Energy Blocks through Colour

T ension is blocked energy — energy trapped in muscles and unable to flow. Nevertheless, tension involves considerable energy, which is why when tense you feel tired and drained. Lying in bed with tense muscles may be a greater drain on your energy than digging the garden all day. This is because in physical work, after an initial impetus effort is reduced in inertia, whereas tightening muscles and sustaining this tension requires constant energy. So paradoxically, hard work may involve less 'work' than so-called rest. Maintaining muscular tension over time uses considerable energy, is progressively tiring, and imposes strain on the body. If you expend too much energy you use excessive adenosine triphosphate or cyclic TCP, the basic chemical used in nerve and muscle cells. Hence your body becomes worn out doing nothing.

People with chronic tension often become locked into a self-perpetuating cycle where although tired their muscular tensions prevent them relaxing or sleeping, further exhausting them so that any action requires more effort. The fundamental problem for such people is that generally they are unaware that they are tense, and because they don't realise that *they* are creating this tension, they don't know how they are doing it, or what they can do to stop it. They are also unaware of the energies tied up by them in maintaining this tension, and its implications for their health, well-being and effective functioning. The following exercise uses colour imagery to help you to assess whether or not you are using your energies effectively.

EXERCISE 2

Find somewhere to sit or lie comfortably with your eyes closed or focused on a fixed point.

Imagine you are lying under a pleasantly warm sun and that you can feel its rays warming but not burning your skin. Imagine that the warmth is penetrating your skin and soothing your aches and pains. As you scan your body slowly from the toes upwards, you can feel it dissolving tension, which is in the form of ice.
This turns to drops of warm fluid which flows in streams through your body and seeps out into the ground through the pores of your skin, leaving your body feeling heavy and warm. Notice any areas where the ice seems particularly dense or resistant to the sun's warmth, focusing your attention on each of these until it has dissolved away.

Continue to scan upwards through your body until all your tensions have dissolved, and having done so focus your attention on your head. Imagine the sun's rays are penetrating your mind, gently dissolving your anxieties, conflicts, confusions, concerns and preoccupations. Allow these to seep away, leaving your mind and body a clear channel without obstruction. Then pay attention to the tensions that have flowed out of you. Imagine that they form an expanse of water. Observe it carefully, noting its significant features and paying particular attention to its colour, clarity, depth and movement. When you are picturing it as vividly as you can, ask yourself the following questions:

1   What might this image tell me about my energies and how effectively I am using them?

2   What can I learn from it?

When you have answered the questions, gradually allow
the image to fade, open your eyes and return to ordinary
consciousness. Then record or write your experience
down, noting the location and nature of your 'energy
blocks', the manner in which they dissolved, and how
easily or otherwise. Also note details of the water imagery,
paying particular attention to the features of colour, clarity,
depth and movement, concluding with an assessment of
what these features might indicate about your energies and
how effectively you are using them.

The following commentary, drawn from observations
made by people who have undertaken this exercise, might
help you to understand your own imagery.

COMMENTARY

The expanse of water imagined in the above exercise is
formed from dissolving tension. It will therefore tend to
reflect the predominant areas of tension within your body
and the energies that are bound up there. Given this, it is
not surprising that some people describe the water they
imagine as red, although red is not a colour usually
associated with water. Indeed it often strikes people as odd
or puzzling if they have no familiarity with esoteric
concepts of subtle energies, chakras and the aura.

The water may be imagined as reflecting the colours
of the setting sun — orange or yellow. Just as the colours
of the setting sun brings an end to the vitalising rays of the
day and onset of night, so too when imagined they suggest
that the person's vital physical and mental energies are
subdued and on the wane.

Green water often impresses us as cold in appearance
and unwelcoming. When imagined in this exercise it
suggests lack of emotional warmth resulting from blocked

heart energies. Blue water suggests that self-expression is ordinarily blocked, and the darker the blue the more likely that the person also lacks insight into her or himself.

Purple water may embody the reflections of mountains, its depths representing an inversion of a person's highest aspiration.

Brown water is often imagined. One man who did so could find no significance in this until he was asked how water becomes brown. John replied by saying that it contained material in suspension such as effluent or sewage, and this corresponded with his experience of himself as 'full of shit'.

Grey water can have a similar significance. Sheila imagined cloudy grey water in which people had washed their dirty clothes, promptly triggering an association with the phrase 'washing dirty linen in public'. She subsequently recognised that this resulted from becoming involved in other people's unpleasant business, and allowing her thinking to become clouded by it.

A black oily or greasy 'film' is sometimes described on the surface of the water, which suggests something having been 'dumped' or imposed on it from elsewhere. This 'pollution' reflects the negativity that often accompanies a person's acting in accordance with the wishes of others rather than expressing herself.

Black water, having absorbed all the possible colour expressed from the body, indicates profound negativity and tension amounting to rigidity and torpor. Black is associated with lack of clarity and vision.

Colour and clarity are often closely connected. The degree of clarity may be an indication of the insight a person has into her or himself.

Unclear areas may indicate unexplored or

unacknowledged aspects of the self, fears, anxieties and other features that people don't wish to look into too closely — their darker aspects — and tend to avoid.

Some people report being unable to see into this water because of reflections, which suggests that their reflection of other things or people — such as social expectations — prevents them seeing their own depths and potential, which as a result are uncharted and unused. Many people's energies are taken up in creating or living up to the images expected by others.

Many people cannot easily determine the extent or depth of the water they imagine. Such people have difficulty in perceiving their own potential. Some people are aware that the water they imagine is part of a bigger expanse of water and that they have far greater potential than they are using. Others are aware of drawing on inexhaustible sources, while some see their sources as limited to a puddle or trickle. Attention to the clarity of water tends to highlight features of depth and limits or boundaries.

Other people recognise that their surface features give a false impression of what is going on below. In some cases the surface of the water may be calm and belie a churning underneath, or the surface may be agitated and wild, but tranquil below. The surface colours may also differ from those beneath. These features suggest the ways in which some people consciously or unwittingly conceal themselves and their true colours, and the difference between their inner and outer selves.

For most people the movement of the water they imagine is striking and significant. It may be sluggish or slow, suggesting insufficient energy; or rushing, frenzied and in some cases dangerously out of control. Dissipation of energy is a common feature of the imagery.

Mike interpreted his dry river in a chalk landscape as reflecting his need to withdraw into himself occasionally to restore his energy. Mavis realised that the waves she saw bobbing up and down on the surface of the water corresponded to her mood cycles. She felt OK when she was 'on the up' and her 'head was above water', but frightened when she was overwhelmed or 'down'.

The movement of the water is usually determined to some extent by the nature of the restrictions on it. Whereas some people imagine the water as expansive, others see it as very confined: constraints that are frequently man-made. Often the water is imagined in swimming pools, fish-tanks, garden ponds, baths or even tumblers, suggesting that the person's energies are limited by artificially created restrictions.

People often feel frustrated or angry that they are held back by such constraints. Marjorie imagined her dissolved tensions taking the form of a swimming pool full of people, and realised that most of her energy went into supporting others.

Mark, who imagined a powerful river cutting a downward V-shape into solid rock, realised that this was taking all his energy but was achieving nothing, as it was not going forward but to a dead end. He recognised that the 'depression' the water was creating in the rock corresponded with his psychological state.

Others see the water as bursting its banks, 'welling up' or as widening its existing boundaries; while others are alarmed to find that it is shrinking or seeping away.

To understand the significance of these images it is important to remember that the water is the product of tensions dissolving in the mind and body. By relating its features back to the source of tension in the head or body, you may be able to identify the source of your tension.

CHAPTER SIX

Energy Balancing through Colour

The previous exercise may have helped you to gain insight into your tensions and the kinds of energy you tend to block, where these blockages are in your body, and how they arise. The exercise should also provide a way of dissolving these blockages, enabling your energies to flow more freely.

The following exercise will give you insight into the way your energies are being used at any time, and offer a way of balancing them so as to attain and maintain optimum health.

EXERCISE 3

Imagine you are sitting directly under a warm sun that is progressively soothing aches, pains and tensions from your mind and body. It seems that the rays of light streaming from the sun are flooding you with protective warmth. You are sitting under a waterfall of light, and you allow yourself time to experience this as fully as possible, to relax and feel at ease.

Imagine that the light cascading from above enters the pores of skin on the crown of your head, where there is a wheel which distributes the light throughout your head. As you observe this, note its size, the direction and character of its movement and how well it is distributing light. Pay careful attention to the predominant colour of light being distributed. As you are doing so, notice that the wheel is like a Catherine wheel distributing sparks of light which shower outwards and downwards. As you follow these downwards, you see that there is another wheel situated at a point midway between your eyebrows, and that it too is distributing light. Once again, note all the features of this wheel, noting its size, direction and speed of movement and its predominant colour.

As you follow the sparks it sends downwards, you realise there are five more wheels positioned along the length of your body at points corresponding with the centre of your throat, the middle of your chest, above and below your navel, and at the base of your spine. In turn you look at each of these wheels as they distribute light, noting in each case their size, direction and character of movement, and predominant colour.

Having observed each closely, look at the entire array of wheels. Note whether they are aligned, and how they compare with each other. Are they similar in size, lying in the same plane, moving in the same direction and at the same speed, or do they differ? If so, note how. Do they appear coordinated, so that the light flows easily between them?

Now look at the base of your spine. Light is seeping from it. You appear to be sitting at the centre of a growing pool of light which is extending away from you in a series of concentric circles. Notice the colours of each of these bands of light, and whether they are pale, dark, dense or patchy. Try to see where in your body any dark blotches or patches of colour are coming from. Imagine this pool of light spreading out and joining with pools of light being produced by other people and things, first those nearest to you, then those further and further away. You now see yourself, all people and all things floating in an endless sea, each like a small ripple or wave on its vast surface. Be aware that all things are interconnected and that by your thoughts, feelings and actions you affect everything else,

just as you are affected by their thoughts, feelings and
actions.

Now return your attention to the wheels of light in
your body. Try and regulate them so that the flow of light
from one to the other is smooth and harmonious; the
sparks they emit are distributed through and around your
body as a rainbow of colour; and the pool of light in
which you are sitting is pale, translucent and iridescent,
like mother of pearl.

Having done so allow the image to fade, gradually
returning yourself to normal, and record your experience.

COMMENTARY

This exercise provides a way of conceptualising the
structure of the chakra–aura system. As imagery provides
reliable information about subtle energies, the exercise
gives you a way of assessing your energy at any time.
Because imagery can also influence these subtle energies,
you can also redirect and balance them.

I provide no introduction to this exercise to avoid
creating expectations. Most people who undertake it have
no prior knowledge about chakras, the aura and the
physical, psychological and spiritual characteristics
traditionally attributed to them. All the same, the
correspondence between them is consistently striking, and
usually enough to persuade the most sceptical of their
validity.

Various features of the wheels as imagined are
significant. People generally have little difficulty in
visualising the energy wheels of the body, although they
may find that some are missing or difficult to picture in
detail. Some people imagine that one or more wheels are
missing. Women particularly report that the throat wheel is

missing completely, or is erratic or sluggish in its movement, which may indicate that many find it difficult to express themselves.

More usually, all the wheels are imagined, but some are not working properly. Sometimes they appear wobbly, 'on pins' like Catherine wheels, and erratic or eccentric in movement, suggesting that these energies are not easily expressed. Anxiety may be a contributory factor, as the phrase 'being on pins' suggests. Lyn, for example, described her throat wheel as 'bumpy' in movement, as though it wanted to move freely but couldn't.

In many cases the wheels differ in size and speed, with each one becoming progressively larger and slower. This conforms to traditional wisdom, which holds that the vibrations of each chakra become progressively more dense, heavy and lower in frequency down the length of the spine. Often all the wheels are of the same size. Generally, the size of a wheel is an indication of its robustness, and of its energetic potential. Small wheels suggest limited energy, whereas large ones suggest the opposite.

The size of the wheel and the quality of its movement are interrelated. A sluggishly moving small wheel may suggest that the limited energy available is being conserved, whereas rapidly moving small wheels may be susceptible to burn-out. Slow-moving, large wheels may be inefficient energy transmitters and large, fast-moving wheels may be chaotic and affect the functioning of the other wheels. However, in many cases there is no gradual progression in size or velocity of the wheels, but a chaotic mixture of large and small wheels moving at different speeds and without uniformity.

Most commonly some wheels are imagined moving

very slowly, sluggishly or not at all, or very rapidly. Wheels that move quickly suggest overactivity. Overactivity in the wheel just above the navel is often described. This is the third or solar plexus chakra, which is associated with the colour yellow and 'heady' intellectual concerns and forcefulness. Where overactivity occurs this invariably indicates stress, resulting from the mind always being 'on the go'. This can increase the susceptibility to stress-related diseases. Where the heart or fourth wheel is overactive the emotions are likely to be overworked and drained, which can affect immunity to physical and emotional disorders.

Where the lower two wheels are overactive 'sparks might fly', quite literally, because these relate to strong passions. Where the red wheel is overactive these passions may become overheated, leading to excess anger or aggression, violence and sexual deviance. Overactivity in the second wheel may produce hyperactivity, which if unchecked may lead to physical exhaustion, excessive eating or drinking and digestive disorders.

Overactivity in the throat or fifth wheel may be associated with talking too much, a tendency to gossip, superficiality, throat problems and even hyperthyroidism. Underactivity reflects the opposite tendencies. Sluggishness in the throat wheel is likely to be associated with hesitancy in speech and self-expression and — in extreme cases — with hypothyroidism or an underactive thyroid.

Sluggishness in the heart wheel is likely to be associated with dulled emotional responses, indifference and reduced immunity. In the yellow wheel it may reflect intellectual dullness or lack of development, and feelings of powerlessness. Underactivity in the second wheel is associated with lack of drive and stamina and poor digestion; and lack of physical vitality, sex drive and productivity with the red wheel.

The direction and quality of movement usually varies considerably from wheel to wheel. Some wheels lie and move in a different plane to others, which can cause problems if the flow of energy from one wheel to another is disrupted. Wheels moving on a horizontal plane tend to distribute light only downwards, rather than in all directions, and may be considered less efficient than wheels moving in a vertical plane. In some cases all the wheels move harmoniously in the same direction.

More typically, one or more wheels move anti-clockwise. These effectively push out the energy available to them rather than distributing it within the body and so block this potential. The energy then manifests in the aura of the individual as colour, and in the present exercise as colour in the pool of light surrounding the person.

The colours of the wheels are always a good indicator of their functioning. It is highly variable, not only from person to person but over time. Many people describe the wheel colours in a way that is fully consistent with the rainbow sequence colours traditionally assigned to the chakras. Where the wheels vibrate harmoniously, a pure bright light may be observed. Others imagine each wheel emitting white light, which is a composite of all colour. Some imagine rainbow colours emanating from each wheel. This imagery suggests a state of balance. But if certain wheels appear to be erratic, over or underactive or moving counterclockwise, this suggests that the current healthy situation is unlikely to continue. Clear 'fluid' light emissions are also associated with wheels that are working well, and gold and silver emissions appear to indicate a harmoniously balanced system.

In many cases the colours traditionally associated with
the chakras have been displaced. So someone may imagine
yellow predominating in some or all wheels, indicating the
predominance of mental energy and a tendency to
rationalise everything. Where red appears in wheels other
than the base it indicates anger and aggression. When it
appears in the second wheel it suggests over-excitement,
hyperactivity, heated passions and potential stomach
problems. When it appears at the solar plexus the person
may have angry thoughts and appear dominant, rude and
threatening to others.

In the heart wheel red represents 'fire' in the heart,
and thus passionate love. If the red deepens into black this
may suggest thwarted passion and a 'broken' or 'bleeding'
heart. Red in the throat wheel indicates a tendency to
express irritation and to inflammation in that area. Jenny,
who imagined red sparks being emitted by this otherwise
blue wheel, admitted that she frequently tends to 'spark
off' rows and ill feeling by her angry outbursts. Where red
appears in the brow wheel it may be a sign of mental
illness, and it may indicate intense spirituality when it
appears at the crown.

Orange is the colour of activity, and it rarely occurs
other than in the lower wheels. In the base wheel it
suggests an active sex life, and in the solar plexus wheel a
lively mind. Yellow, the colour of rationality, often displaces
other colours and indicates the tendency to analyse
everything. When it appears in the base wheel it suggests
that sex tends to be governed by the mind, and in the
second wheel it suggests that gut feelings and passions are
under rational control. Where it occurs in the heart wheel
it indicates that the head rules the heart. Yellow appearing
in the throat wheel is often a sign of the need to be seen

to be clever. Some yellow in the brow wheel indicates insightful understanding, whereas too much can suggest scepticism. When it appears in the purple wheel, yellow shows that spiritual issues are dealt with intellectually rather than known and experienced directly.

Many people lack green in the heart wheel, showing that their heart isn't in their current endeavours. Dark green in this wheel indicates possessiveness and envy, as the well-known phrase suggests. When it appears in the second wheel it suggests emotional sensitivity, but if excessive it may indicate emotional vulnerability and a sensitive digestion. In the red wheel it indicates that the heart is in one's sex life. If green does not appear in the solar plexus wheel this indicates a detached and analytical approach to life. Similarly, some green in the throat wheel is desirable, otherwise the person communicates little warmth and kindness and lacks sincerity. Turquoise, which combines blue and green, is associated with sincerity and genuineness, and often appears in this wheel. Too much green in this wheel, however, indicates too much kindness and the possibility of being exploited. Green in the brow wheel indicates generosity of spirit and in the crown wheel, compassion.

Wherever it appears, sky blue is suggestive of coolness. In the base wheel it indicates a cool attitude to sex, and in the second wheel is a sign of poor health and appetite. In the solar plexus it indicates a cool, clear head, whereas in the heart wheel it indicates emotional detachment and difficulty in forming relationships. When blue appears in the brow wheel and in the crown it indicates healing ability. Dark blue, or indigo, indicates impartiality wherever it appears, and purple or violet reflect aesthetic and spiritual qualities.

Generally the colours seen in the pool of light around the base wheel tend to correspond with anomalies in the relevant wheels. As such, the imagery reflects the correspondence between chakra functioning and the appearance of the aura.

People who describe their base wheel as black may feel that they have no vitality whatever. Brown indicates stagnant energies and withdrawal. In the base wheel it indicates lack of sexual fulfilment, and in the second wheel a lack of physical and emotional vitality. In the solar plexus it may be a sign of mental withdrawal and depression.

In the heart wheel brown is often a sign of grief, loss and susceptibility to disease. Brown in the throat wheel indicates a tendency to withdraw from communication with others and to speech problems. In the brow, brown indicates a tendency to withdraw from the outside world, and in the crown wheel it is connected with loss of faith, belief and purpose in life.

Many traditional practices are based on the belief that it is possible to receive information about subtle energies by way of imagery, and so chakra functioning can be reliably and accurately assessed in this and other ways. These practices also advocate visualisation as a way to influence mental and bodily functions. Modifications of imagery such as speeding or slowing certain wheels, changing the direction or quality of movement, effecting repairs in damaged or dysfunctional wheels, and changing their colour, may have benefits. This is the experience of many people who have described changes in their mental and physical condition corresponding with deliberately induced changes in their imagery.

The first time Fiona tried this exercise she discovered that all her wheels were moving sluggishly and were uncoordinated. She repeated the exercise daily for some time, imagining that the wheels were moving harmoniously and fairly forcefully in the same direction until she could 'see' that they were emitting white light. As she did so, Fiona noted considerable improvements in her overall health and well-being, both psychological and physical. Andrew noted a change in the direction of his brow wheel over a three-month period, and attributed this to the increased insight he had gained as a result of using imagery in the development of self-awareness.

PART THREE

Developing Your True Colours

CHAPTER SEVEN

Breathing in Colour

The exercises in Part Two may have given you some insight into the colours with which you resonate and those with which you don't; the personal energies these relate to; the extent to which you are using your energies effectively; the energies whose expression you tend to block, and their implications for your life and general well-being. The following exercises will help you to 'own' the energies you currently disown, reject and project on to others and the environment, and to experiment by bringing more colour into your life. This should enable you to promote all your energies and express your full potential.

Most people respond to unpleasant experiences by blocking their feelings. To do this they have to stop or slow down the energy flow through the relevant chakra, which affects its functioning in several ways. It may become blocked with stagnant energy, spin irregularly or anti-clockwise, become disfigured or distorted, and eventually result in the development of a physical problem. However, this process not only generates illness but also the individual's reality, as Barbara Brennan explains:

> Since chakras are not only metabolisers of energy, but also devices that sense energy, they serve to tell us about the world around us. If we 'close' chakras, we do

not let information come in. *Thus, when we make our chakras flow counterclockwise, we send our energies out into the world, sense what the energy is that we send out and say that this is the world. This is called projection in psychology.* (Italics in the original text.)

Thus energy that should be drawn into the chakra is projected out into the energy field surrounding the body, where it manifests as colour, forming the filters through which the person sees the world. It colours his or her outlook on life, and determines the way he or she seems to others. The person who closes the base chakra energies relating to basic energies and functions will project the corresponding energy into his environment and will tend to 'see red'. His anger and aggression will tend to be projected on to others and, because he believes these energies arise in them rather than himself and are directed to rather than by him, he will probably feel insecure and lacking in confidence, act defensively and feel justified in doing so. He will seem angry, irritable and somewhat unstable to others.

The person who closes off his gut feelings will have passionate views, and will seem excitable, easily aroused and difficult to others. People who close their solar plexus energies will project their mental powers, power and mastery on to others. Accordingly they will see others as intimidating and powerful and themselves as victims. To others they will appear passive and even cowardly (or 'yellow'). Everything will be coloured by emotion for those who project their heart energy. They will see others as more valued and accepted than themselves, and will appear envious and resentful, as in the phrase 'green with envy'. They may have difficulty forming and maintaining relationships.

The person who projects his throat energies may see others as cool and distant and be seen by them as remote, reserved and uncommunicative, or shy. Someone who projects brow energies will see 'as through a glass darkly'. Everything will appear to be mystifying, impenetrable and unclear to him, and to others he will appear subdued, depressed, 'blue'. When someone projects crown energies, she will tend to see life through a purple haze and will have difficulty perceiving ordinary reality. To others she will seem 'way out', detached and unworldly.

Closure of any chakra represents complete denial of feeling in a certain area. It is clearly an extreme reaction which, if sustained, will inevitably have unfortunate psychological and physical consequences. More typically chakras are not completely closed but partially blocked, so that some but not all of their energy is projected outwards. This will colour the person's outlook, but less consistently than if the chakra is completely closed. The first step in healing with colour is to reverse the tendency of people to project certain energies and thereby 'colour' their life in ways that might lead to problems. From the exercises in Part Two, particularly Exercise 3 (page 76) which relates to chakra functioning and the appearance of the aura, you may have a fairly good idea of the energies you typically project outwards and the ways these 'colour' your outlook on life and influence your well-being.

One way in which you can reverse this process is by breathing in colour. This has long been a feature of traditional healing practices and is widely used in contemporary colour therapy. There are numerous variations of this practice, and it is advisable to experiment with several until you find one that seems best suited to your needs.

EXERCISE 4

The basic technique involves simply sitting or lying and establishing an easy, rhythmic breathing pattern.

Then, as you focus on your breathing, imagine breathing in colour. If you realise that you tend to block certain energies, focus on the relevant chakra and imagine breathing light of an appropriate colour into it. Try not to think of this colour, because thought is itself a 'yellow' energy, but to sense it as fully as possible. If you are uncertain which energies you tend to block, just focus on your breathing and receive any colour that emerges. As it does so, continue to breathe in the colour and note any sensations that arise.

If you find that breathing in colour is difficult — most usually this happens if you are trying too hard — simply allow yourself to relax by breathing in sunlight. Imagine that you are sitting or lying in warm sunshine and breathing its energy into your body. Be aware of any thoughts, impressions, sensations or other experiences that arise as you do so.

COMMENTARY

Many people find that it is very easy to imagine breathing in sunlight and much less easy to imagine breathing in colour. Some find it helpful to breathe in through their nose and out through their mouth, and in the Chinese tradition to imagine that as they breathe in light it travels down their spine to its base and then upwards, filling the body with light and pushing out 'fog' through the mouth. Breathing in this way for a few minutes is usually enough to promote relaxation. When this happens you may find that colours begin to present themselves quite spontaneously. If they do, just carry on breathing in that way, being aware as you do so of any sensations or impressions.

A fascinating account of the insights and benefits that can derive from colour breathing is provided by Jane. She first tried to breathe in the colour she thought appropriate to her most obvious energy blocks as revealed in previous exercises, and found it very difficult. So she imagined simply sitting under a warm sun and focusing her attention on her crown chakra. Suddenly and unexpectedly she gained a startling insight into how she was blocking her energy. She realised that the religious indoctrination of her childhood had 'turned her off' religion. Her convent school education had left her with various hang ups, and led to her rejecting the principles and practices of organised religion.

Jane realised that much of her denial of religion resulted from being hurt by one particularly punitive teacher, and that her experience had coloured her attitude to the religious in general. As she did so she 'saw' a vivid purple and by breathing in harmony with it she felt a great sense of relief. She discovered blockages in her throat chakra in relation to the way she expressed herself in certain contexts. As she had always thought of herself as very self-expressive, this surprised her, but again Jane realised that painful experiences — this time in the workplace — had led her to suppress a good deal there. She found that as this insight emerged so too did a vivid colour, in this case a brilliant sky blue.

By now totally absorbed in the process, Jane continued to examine each chakra in turn, and found that in each case she tended to block the energies in ways she had not appreciated before, and that fear of being hurt had led to this restriction of her energies. Subsequently she found that simply by focusing on each chakra, the appropriate colour would emerge and she could further her insights into its functioning. Over time Jane found significant changes occurring as she did so, and greatly enhanced feelings of well-being.

CHAPTER EIGHT

Letting Colour Go To Your Head

Pat has participated in several of my workshops and also in one-to-one therapy with me. In one session she revealed that when she had attempted the wheel exercise (see Chapter Six) she had unaccountably found herself imagining hats. The experience had been so powerful that she had not only written it down but had also drawn some of the images she had received and brought them along to show me. When exploring these pictures with her and the valuable insights she got from them, I realised she had hit on a potentially useful exercise. I developed it systematically and 'tested' it on other people.

Some time later, Pat told me of her surprise and delight to find a book in her local library by the psychologist Edward de Bono. She had been attracted by its title *Six Thinking Hats*. She was even more astonished on reading it to discover the striking similarity between her spontaneous imagery and that in the book. In his book, de Bono advocates wearing six different hats in order to promote different styles of thinking:

> *A white hat* for neutral, objective, factual thinking.
> *A red hat* for thinking that allows feelings, emotions, hunches and intuition of the thinker or others to be explored.
> *A black hat* for thinking that is specifically concerned with negative assessment — pointing out what is wrong, or in error, and identifying risks, dangers and disadvantages.
> *A yellow hat* for positive, constructive and optimistic

thinking which explores and finds logical support for value and benefit, producing concrete proposals and suggestions, and 'making things happen'.

A green hat for creative thinking that is adaptable and generates new concepts and perceptions.

A blue hat for controlled, organised, disciplined thinking of the kind expected in summaries, overviews and conclusions.

The basis message of de Bono seems to be: 'if the cap fits, wear it'. A similar principle applies to the following exercise.

EXERCISE 5

Sitting or lying comfortably with your eyes closed, focus your attention on your pubic bone. Allow yourself some time to become aware of the sensations in this area. As you do so, allow the image of a red hat to form as vividly as possible and note your reactions to it. Try it on your head and wear it. Observe where you go and what you do while you have it on, and your feelings and thoughts as you do so.

Now focus your attention on the area some two inches below your navel, becoming aware of the sensation there. As you do so, allow the image of an orange hat to form. Put it on and wear it, observing where you go, what you do, how you feel and think.

In the same way, imagine a yellow hat forming in response to the sensations you experience just above your navel in the solar plexus; a green hat forming at the centre of your chest; a sky blue hat at your throat; a dark blue hat in the centre of the eyebrows and a purple hat at the crown of your head. Imagine trying on and wearing each hat, noting your behaviour, feelings and thoughts as you do so.

When you have allowed all the images to form, open your eyes and record what happened.

COMMENTARY

Most people thoroughly enjoy this exercise and are amused by it. Red energy relates to the base chakra, which is associated with basic vitality, sexuality and productivity. It energises the feet, legs and pelvis and its function is to maintain a basic sense of grounding or security. People with positive red energy are likely to have their feet firmly on the ground, to feel rooted and have a good sense of reality.

In response to this exercise people frequently imagine themselves wearing red hats when engaged in physical activities, especially when participating in or spectating at sporting events, and feeling lively, energetic, excited, flamboyant and sexy. 'Red hat' activities are often associated with status, and therefore with a person's social 'standing'. Women in particular tend to feel confident, smart, sophisticated and 'uplifted' in red. People tend also to feel more secure in their personal relationships when wearing red. By expressing more red energy in your life you may be able to enhance your energy, vitality, security and self-confidence.

Orange energy is associated with the second chakra, and with powerful instinctive feelings. It is basic, physical and unrefined. Orange hats reflect this, generally being associated with energetic activities such as sport, dance, play and laughter; and with childish interests such as parties, games, circuses and clowns — that is, all the activities most people feel obliged not to engage in as they grow up. Most adults fail fully to express their 'orange' energies, and need to relax in this area.

This can be achieved by surrendering to the orange hat imagery rather than resisting it. When Bernard imagined himself in a large orange floppy hat in which he wanted to laugh hilariously at nothing at all until he fell over, he merely allowed himself a smile and a suppressed chuckle. He didn't want to be seen as a fool by others for laughing out loud. Few people fail to feel the benefit of a 'belly laugh' and for this reason certain Indian traditions advocate a form of breathing which requires the person to rapidly and repeatedly expel their breath. This produces a 'ha ha' sound, which when repeated quickly leads to genuine laughter and so is believed therapeutic. This can be combined with colour breathing.

Green energy associated with the heart chakra relates to connectedness and relationship, not only with others but all creation. Typically, when people imagine wearing green hats they reflect the outdoor life. 'Robin Hood' styles are often described, as are waxed weatherproof hats, riding caps, and fashionable styles such as might be worn to the races. People wearing these hats may describe feeling 'lovely' or engaged in an activity they love, whether this is dog walking or gardening. These feelings can be enhanced by expressing your green energy.

Sky blue energy is associated with the throat chakra, and thus with speech and self-expression. Those who imagine wearing hats of this colour often describe feeling 'cool'; this is typically reflected in boating or sailing hats and skiing caps. Wearing these hats can be a liberating experience, reflecting some activity a person has always wanted to try but never has, such as ice skating, dancing or skiing.

When wearing blue hats many people, especially men, express themselves in ways they often describe as silly, which is no doubt a reflection of the inhibiting effects of social pressure towards seriousness rather than frivolity. Indeed social convention precludes a good deal of male expression. John, who imagined himself wearing a blue nurse's cap and carrying a stethoscope, described himself as 'helping people and doing silly things like that'.

Women may also be liberated from stereotypes of appropriate feminine behaviour when wearing blue hats. Cathy, who imagined herself in a blue mortar board at a graduation ceremony, recognised this as an indication that she fails to express her intellectual energies fully. Ann found that when wearing a blue hat she could be more assertive.

Dark blue is associated with the brow chakra, with insight, imagination and intuitive abilities. Commonly hats of this colour are associated with occupational groups such as nurses, police and fire officers, train and taxi drivers, chauffeurs, pilots, sailors and the armed services, which all share a commitment to serving others. This is intriguing because in ancient traditions the third eye or brow chakra is associated with service to God or gods, fellow human beings and other creatures.

Surprisingly, however, these commonplace hats do not often feature in the above exercise. The hats described tend to be idiosyncratic, such as a many-tiered Chinese pagoda. Sultan's hats are often described. They tend to reflect far-sightedness and heightened perception. Julie described herself in one such hat flying off on a magic carpet to 'see what is going on elsewhere'. Jamie saw himself wearing a turban with a huge central jewel that enabled him to see all kinds of distant and future happenings.

Purple is associated with the crown chakra, with spiritual energies, enlightenment and transcendence of ordinary reality. Archbishops' mitres, papal crowns, wimples, wizards' and witches caps, triangular or conical headwear such as favoured by Pharaohs, have all been described in connection with this chakra. People typically describe feeling taller and 'above things' when wearing these hats. Feelings of power, raised consciousness, otherworldliness, transcendence and ecstasy have also been reported, and a sense of purpose. These feelings can be enhanced through expressing purple energy.

By experimenting with the various hats in the exercise it is possible to experience the thoughts, feelings, actions and reactions that result from liberating the energies of your chakras rather than blocking them. So you will get some sense of how you might be if you were to encourage and develop the expression of your true colours rather than inhibit them.

CHAPTER NINE

Managing Pain with Colour Imagery

I have suggested that in order to avoid unpleasant feelings, people slow down or stop the transmission of energy from the relevant chakras, which eventually leads to psychological and physical problems. The experiences most likely to be avoided are those that cause pain, whether physical or emotional. Blocking pain in this way leads to tension, which often actually increases existing physical pain, and generates others. It also sets up a chain of events that may produce disease — both psychological and physical — and further pain. Ultimately being 'at pains' to avoid pain by blocking unpleasant feelings is self-defeating. Indeed pain can be conceived as both a cause and effect of blocked energy.

As we have seen, colour imagery provides a valuable indication of and insight into the nature and location of energy blockages within the body — not only of existing tensions and pain but also of potential pains. Imagery can also be used to relax these tensions and pains and to promote and regulate the healthy flow of energy within the body. It can be used to modify pain, and is valuable not only in assessing but also in managing and treating pain. The following exercise is both simple and highly effective.

EXERCISE 6

Relax as fully as possible in whatever way suits you best. Then identify areas of residual pain in your body, or those areas in which pain tends to occur. Focusing your attention on each of these areas one at a time, allow an image to form in response to the sensations you experience there. Try not to influence or censor it in any way. If nothing comes to mind, don't 'try' to produce an image — simply allow yourself to relax further while keeping a steady focus on the area in question. When an image arises note its features, paying particular attention to colour, shape and size, and noting any thoughts, memories or impressions. Ask yourself what you can learn about your pain from this image. You may find that you can interact with it. If so, ask it what it is doing there and why; what it is doing or can do for you, and what you can do for it.

Now try to change the colour of the image, and as you do so, notice any sensations in your body and your mental and emotional reactions. Then change its shape and its size. Experiment with as many changes as you can, and take note of your physical, mental and emotional reactions as you do so. Next, shrink the pain and project it out of your body as far as you can, until it is out of sight. If you wish to, allow the pain to reappear and to return to its former position in your body, noting as it does so any changes in sensation. Then allow the image to fade, return to ordinary awareness and record your experience.

COMMENTARY

When asked to draw their pain, adults and children usually use the colours black, red, orange, brown, and less often purple and green. The more intense the pain the more likely they are to use red and black and to produce large drawings. Children typically draw spiky, angular abstract shapes to depict acute pain, reflecting the sensation of 'sharpness'. Less acute pain is shown as smoother, with curved rather than jagged outlines. Adults are less likely to draw abstract shapes than children, and more likely to add words and phrases.

Few people have any trouble creating images of their pain. Close examination of the various features of the images can yield valuable insights. For many people, however, the effects of changing their imagery in various ways are striking and dramatic. By doing so they discover that they have a degree of control over their pain, and therefore their experience of it.

Some people find that changing the colour of the pain has immediate effects. Changing red and orange pains to blue or green can produce relief. Tension and migraine headaches respond well to blue, which generally appears to have a soothing effect when substituted for other colours. Sensations that appear as 'black and blue' respond well to red and orange; and when the colour of pain is vivid, simply diluting it can bring about marked improvement in reducing the pain.

Experimenting with colour should reveal which is most appropriate to a particular pain, but some indication as to the nature and source of the pain, and the most appropriate way of managing it, may be provided by the colour or colours of the initial image. Whereas red and orange are associated with physical pains, the musculo-skeletal system and the lower areas of the body, yellow pain suggests the possibility of rather more mental issues; mental stress should be considered as a major underlying or contributory factor, together with related things such as fear and anxiety.

Where green appears, emotional factors and personal relationships play a part. When blue is a factor you may need to consider who or what is a 'pain in the neck' for you, or even whether you are a 'pain' and how this affects your self-expression and the way you are seen by others. Dark blue also raises the possibility of mental or psychological factors such as depression underlying or contributing to pain. Purple pain may indicate despair, and loss of hope, direction and purpose. Black, brown and grey all suggest negativity, and that denial plays a significant role in the pain experience.

It may seem strange that the exercise allows people to restore their pain to its original site, and that instead people would be pleased to rid themselves of it and would not want it back. Yet for many people the idea of their pain disappearing completely produces anxiety. On closer examination it usually emerges that these people need their pain because it meets some important function in their life. It may be a way of gaining the attention of others; or it may relieve them from unpleasant and unwanted roles or obligations. If you find that you are one of those reluctant or unable to let your pain disappear entirely, ask yourself what function it serves in your life, and whether it is possible to meet this need in another, less painful way.

Changing the colour, shape and size of pain can have immediate and lasting effects. You might expect that in most cases the relief experienced is only short-term and that the pain will return. Certainly if you expect the pain to return it probably will, because this amounts to inviting it to do so. However, if you can achieve even fleeting relief from pain this may be enough to persuade you that you have power to control it, and that with practice you can develop this ability and extend the pain-free periods. During her first attempt at visualisation of this kind, Cathy experienced relief from a long-standing hip injury resulting from years of dance training. This persuaded her to continue, and after two weeks she was pain-free and able to wear high-heeled court shoes for the first time in years. June successfully treated a long-standing knee injury, and Fred overcame long-standing tennis elbow. Shirley gained significant relief from her rheumatoid arthritis by modifying her green imagery.

Many of those people who successfully use colour imagery come to realise the truth of the words Kahlil Gibran puts into the mouth of *The Prophet*:

> Much of your pain is self-chosen.
> It is the bitter potion by which the physician
>   within you heals your sick self.

CHAPTER TEN

Bringing Colour into Your Life

Through imaginative use of colour, it is possible to realise your full potential and so promote spiritual, psychological and physical well-being, or health in its true sense. These brief guidelines will help you to bring more colour into your life.

Red energises the feet, legs, pelvis, hip joints, base of the spine, prostate, testes and urogenital tract. It stimulates physical activity and vitality, feelings of security, stability, self-confidence and warmth.

To bring more *red* into your life:

breathe in red;

visualise red;

meditate on the colour red, red flowers, gemstones and crystals;

wear red;

surround yourself with red;

place in your surroundings and wear gemstones and crystals such as garnet, ruby, red jasper, bloodstone, black tourmaline and smoky quartz;

use essential oils Myrrh, Patchouli and Vetivert in burners, inhalers, massage and baths;

eat red meat, red-skinned vegetables and fruit, such as: beetroot, radishes, red peppers, tomatoes, cherries, strawberries, kidney beans, chilli peppers, and spices such as clove, cumin, chilli and cayenne pepper.

Use any of the above in rooms or buildings where increased physical activity is required, and in children's playrooms;

if you feel tired, run down or physically weak;

if you are cold;

if you are starting a head cold;

if you have problems of physical mobility, pains or stiffness in your legs;

if you have sciatica;

if you suffer from lower back pain;

if you have varicose veins;

if you have poor circulation;

if you are anaemic;

if you have reproductive problems;

if you are infertile;

if you are impotent;

if you have prostate gland problems;

if you feel alone, unsupported and insecure.

Do not use:

with hyperactive, violent or aggressive children and adults, in work situations where potentially dangerous machinery is in use, where concentration is needed, for reading, or in bedrooms;

if you are angry or feeling aggressive;

if you are bleeding or suffer from haemorrhoids;

if you have inflamed cuts and wounds;

if you have infectious wounds;

if you suffer from high blood pressure;

if you have heart problems;

if you have eyestrain;

if you are accident prone;

if you want to relax.

Orange energises the liver, spleen, pancreas, kidneys and bladder. It stimulates the metabolism, digestion, detoxification, immunity to disease, physical and emotional energies, sexuality, athletic performance and physical appetites, and regulates the sugar and fluid balance of the body.

To bring more *orange* into your life:
breathe in orange;
visualise orange;
meditate on the colour orange, orange flowers, gemstones
    and minerals;
wear orange;
surround yourself with orange;
place in your surroundings and wear amber, carnelian,
    coral and peach aventurine;
use essential oils Sandalwood, Cardamum and Ginger in
    burners, inhalers, massage and baths;
eat oranges, tangerines, mandarins, apricots, melon,
    persimmon, papaya, carrots, orange peppers, lentils, and
    spices such as cinnamon, cloves, ginger and ginseng.

Use it in playrooms, exercise rooms, dance studios and
sports halls, or where social gatherings take place;
if you have low energy;
if you feel lethargic or bored;
if you want to increase vitality;
if you want to enhance your sexuality;
if you feel depressed;
if you are inhibited;
if you need more energy to cope with the demands of
    everyday activities;
if you want to feel happy;

if you want to be playful and have fun;

if you want to stimulate your appetite;

if you have bladder problems or urinary tract infections
such as cystitis;

if you have rheumatism;

if you lack sex drive;

if you have feelings of sexual inadequacy;

if you don't experience orgasm;

if you have menstrual difficulties or female dysfunctions
such as vaginal infections, ovarian cysts, endometriosis,
fibroids.

Do not use:

in rest rooms;

if you tend to overeat or drink;

if you overindulge in sexual or sporting activities;

if you suffer from any addictions;

if you use stimulants;

if you suffer from nausea;

if you tend to be argumentative, angry, irritable;

if you have intestinal problems, irritable bowel syndrome,
colitis, pancreatitis, diabetes, liver and kidney problems,
hepatitis, gall bladder problems or adrenal gland
dysfunction;

if you suffer from incontinence;

if you want to relax.

Yellow energises the adrenal glands, the sympathetic
nervous system and thereby the muscles, heartbeat, digestion
and circulation. It stimulates the digestive tract, mental
activity, mental clarity, verbal reasoning and will power.

To bring *yellow* into your life:

breathe in yellow;

visualise yellow;

meditate on the colour yellow, yellow flowers and
    minerals;

wear yellow;

surround yourself with yellow;

place in your surroundings and wear citrine, topaz, tiger's
    eye, yellow zircon, yellow jasper, gold and gold topaz;

use essential oils Citronella and Lemon in burners,
    inhalers, massage and baths;

eat yellow peppers, corn, grapefruit, melons, bananas,
    lemons, pineapple, eggs, cheese, yellow lentils, chickpeas
    and spices such as turmeric, mace, mustard and saffron.

Use it in reading rooms and studies, where social
gatherings take place and lively conversation is required,
and in the decor of rooms and buildings in which children
with learning difficulties work;

if you are suffering mental fatigue;

if you feel mentally dull;

if your decision making is poor;

if your memory is poor;

if you need to concentrate;

if you are sitting an examination;

if you have difficulty learning anything;

if you need to be objective;

if you feel nervous or fearful;

if you feel disempowered and submissive;

if you want to feel optimistic and confident;

if you have poor digestion.

Do not use:

with hyperactive, behaviourally disordered or aggressive
    children and adults;

if you are feeling restless;

if you are suffering from stress or a stress-related disorder;

if you cannot switch off mentally;

if you want to rest and relax;

if you suffer from insomnia;

if you are aggressive or prone to violence;

if you suffer from stomach disorders;

if you suffer from stomach ulcers, acute indigestion or
nausea.

Green energises the thymus gland. It stimulates the heart, lungs, bronchia, arms, hands, skin, secondary circulation and the immune system. It promotes positive feelings, compassion and sensitivity.

To bring more *green* into your life:

breathe in green;

visualise green;

meditate on the colour green, green plants, gemstones and
minerals;

wear green;

surround yourself with it;

walk in the countryside, buy houseplants, take up
gardening;

use essential oils Pine, Bergamot, Inula and Melissa in
burners, inhalers, massage and baths;

place in your surroundings and wear emerald, malachite,
tourmaline, green agate, beryl, green jade, green
aventurine, chrysoprase and rose quartz;

wear copper;

eat all green fruits and vegetables, avocado pears, olives and
mung beans.

Use in any rooms, buildings, workshops or studios where peace and calmness is desired, sensitivity is needed or activities involve physical touch;

if you need to calm down;

if you are anxious;

if you feel bitter or resentful towards others or have relationship problems;

if you find it difficult to give of yourself to others;

if you lack compassion;

if you want to develop your sensitivity;

if you feel 'out of touch';

if you are working with your hands;

if your heart is not in any aspect of your life or work;

if you have hypertension;

if you have heart problems;

if you have circulation difficulties;

if you have breathing problems such as asthma or bronchitis;

if you suffer from immune-deficiency;

if you have tumours, cancer or AIDS;

if you have arthritis or rheumatism;

if you suffer from allergies;

if you have skin disorders;

if you suffer from chronic disease;

if you have upper back and shoulder problems.

Do not use:

in laboratories or rooms where detached analytical thinking is required;

if you suffer from auto-immune disease.

Sky blue energises the thyroid gland and thereby the metabolism, the body's temperature control. It stimulates the voice, self-expression, communication, personal responsibility and hearing.

To bring more *blue* into your life:

breathe in blue;

visualise blue;

meditate on blue, the sky, sea, water, the colour blue, blue
    flowers, gemstones and minerals;

wear blue;

surround yourself with blue;

place in your surroundings and wear turquoise,
    chrysocolla, blue topaz, sodalite, aquamarine, azurite and
    kyanite gemstones and minerals;

use essential oils Lavender, Chamomile and Geranium in
    burners, inhalers, massage and baths;

eat fish, blue-skinned fruits such as plums and blueberries,
    and asparagus.

Use in bedrooms, rest rooms, clinics, any room or building
    used for clinical procedures, dairies, cold stores;

if you need to calm your mind or nerves;

if you want to relax;

if you want to cool down physically, mentally or
    emotionally;

in cases of fever;

if you suffer from insomnia;

in cases of shock;

if you are bleeding;

if you have boils, haemorrhoids, inflamed or septic cuts
    and wounds, burns or sunburn;

if you have swollen glands;

if you suffer from psoriasis, skin conditions or irritations;

if you have insect bites or stings;

if you have ear, nose or throat problems;

if your voice is weak or you lose your voice;

if you cannot speak up for yourself;

if you suffer from embarrassment;

if you have a speech impediment;

if you have a stiff neck;

if you suffer from headache, tension headaches or
   migraine.

Do not use:

if you feel cold and shivery;

if you suffer from thyroid deficiency or slow metabolism.

Dark blue or indigo energises the pineal gland. It
stimulates the lower brain, the central nervous system and
the endocrine system — notably the hormones serotonin
and melatonin. It thereby stimulates hormonal activity
throughout the body, unconscious processes, imagination,
insight, intuition and psychic abilities.

To bring more *indigo* into your life:

breathe indigo;

visualise indigo;

meditate on indigo and dark blue, the late evening sky,
   blue minerals and gemstones;

wear indigo;

surround yourself with indigo;

place in your surroundings and wear gems and minerals
   such as lapis lazuli, sodalite, sapphire and azurite;

use essential oils Patchouli and Frankincense in burners,
   inhalers, massage and baths;

eat dark blue vegetables and fruits such as aubergines,
   plums, bilberries and grapes.

Use in rooms where contemplation and meditation take
place;

if you need to calm your nerves;

if you are agitated;

if you have problems sleeping;

if you feel restless;

if you need to think clearly and with insight;

if you lack imagination;

if you need to use or develop your intuition;

if you suffer with migraine.

Do not use:

in play rooms or centres of physical activity;

if you are depressed;

if you suffer from Seasonal Affective Disorder, eating
    disorders such as anorexia and bulimia nervosa,
    infertility or menstrual irregularities;

if you suffer from mental illness;

if you have nightmares;

if you feel melancholy and sad;

if you fear paranormal or psychic phenomena;

if you are taking sedatives.

Purple or violet energises the pituitary gland. It stimulates
the upper brain and the nervous system, and creativity,
inspiration, aestheticism, artistic ability and high ideals.

If you want to bring more *purple* into your life:

breathe purple or violet;

visualise purple or violet;

meditate on the colour purple, purple flowers, mountains,
    gemstones and minerals;

wear purple and violet;

surround yourself with purple or violet;

walk in the mountains;

place in your surroundings and wear amethyst, alexandrite,

sugalite, purple fluorite, selenite, diamond, clear quartz and aragonite;

use essential oils Lavender, Elemi and Frankincense in burners, inhalers, massage and baths;

eat purple-skinned fruits and vegetables such as aubergines, grapes, asparagus and red cabbage.

Use where you want to inspire artistic, creative, aesthetic and imaginative activities and spirituality, facilitate clear focus and awareness and meditation; in theatres, children's classrooms;

if you need inspiration;

if you lack imagination;

if you need clarity of mind and purpose;

if you wish to meditate;

if you want to engage in visualisation;

if you want to develop spiritually;

if you lack faith in yourself, others, or the divine;

if you have lost your faith;

if you are striving for meaning and purpose in life;

if you are depressed;

if you suffer from paralysis or debilitating conditions such as multiple sclerosis.

Do not use:

in rooms used for entertaining or where you want to encourage conversation, or in rooms and buildings occupied by the mentally ill, especially those suffering delusions or depersonalisation or with a tendency to be withdrawn;

if you have serious psychological problems;

if you have problems with alcohol or drugs;

if you feel alienated.

Helpful Addresses

The International Association of Colour Therapy
(affiliated to the Institute of Complementary Medicine)
PO Box 3688, London SW13 0XA.

International School for Colour Therapy
73 Elm Bank Gardens, Barnes, London SW13 0NX.

Margaret Cockbain and Mike Booth
Aura Soma, Dev Aura, Little London, Tetford, Lincs.

Colour Energy Corporation
PO Box 1743, Station A, Vancouver V6C 2P7, British
Columbia, Canada.

Theo Gimbel, The Hygeia College of Colour Therapy,
Brook House, Avening, Tetbury, Glos GL8 8NS.

Helen Graham, Dept of Psychology,
McKay Building, Keele University, Keele, Staffs ST5 5BG.

Know Yourself Through Colour Marie Louise Lacy,
3a Bath Road, Worthing, Sussex BN11 3NU.

June McLeod, 5 Dennis Park Crescent, Wimbledon
Chase, London SW20 8QH.

The Maitreya School of Healing
33 Shaftesbury Road, London NI9 4QW.

Howard and Dorothy Sun, Living Colour,
33 Lancaster Grove, Hampstead, London NW3 4EX.

Pauline Wills
9 Wyndale Avenue, Kingsbury, London NW9 9PT.

IRELAND

Philomena Brady
Walmer House, Station Road, Raheny, Dublin 5.

Catherine Campbell
51 St Lawrence Road, Clontarf, Dublin 3.

Mary Stewart Carroll
14 Idrone Close, Knocklyon Woods, Dublin 16.

May Coyle
Bellurgan Point, Dundalk, Co. Louth.

Kay Cranwell
60 Broadford Rise, Ballinteer, Dublin 16.

Lainey Ennis
44 Belgrave Square West, Monkstown, Co. Dublin.

Aveen Ferguson
114 Millview Lawns, Malahide, Co. Dublin.

Mary Higgins
Creesil, Tydavnet, Co. Monaghan.

Christine McGuinness
Back To Nature, Main Street, Cavan, Co. Cavan.

Fania Mahony
The Garden Flat, The Old Rectory, Drumcar, Co. Louth.

Anne O'Hanlon
4 Foxbank, Old Bawn, Tallaght, Dublin 24.

Bernadette Raferty
St Therese, Parson Street, Maynooth, Co. Kildare.

Bernadette Tierney
Flat 4, c/o Dunnes, Main Street, Celbridge, Co. Kildare.

PRODUCTS

Colour Energy Products
Nordraaksgt 8, 0260, Oslo, Norway.

Hygeia Manufacturing Ltd Hygeia Studios,
Brook House, Avening, Tetbury, Glos GL8 8NS.

116

Recommended Reading

Aaranson, B.S., 'Color perception and affect', *American Journal of Clinical Hypnosis* 14 (1971), 38–42.

Anderson, J., *Brain/Mind Bulletin* 15, 4 (1990), 1.

Bell, A.H. ed., *Practical Dowsing: A Symposium,* London: G. Bell & Sons 1965.

Birren, F., *Colour Psychology and Colour Therapy,* New York: Citadel Press, Carol Publishing Group 1992.

Brace, A., 'Experts hail cure for child dyslexia', The *Mail on Sunday,* 27 June 1993, 10.

Branson, L., 'Chromotherapy: nature's healing rainbow', *Attitudes* (Spring 1988), 4–7.

Brennan, B.A., *Hands of Light: A Guide to Healing Through The Human Energy Field,* New York: Bantam 1988.

Costigan, K., 'How colour goes to your head', *Science Digest* (December 1984).

Davidson, J., *Subtle Energy,* Saffron Walden: C.W. Daniel Co. 1987.

Davis, P., *Subtle Aromatherapy,* Saffron Walden: C.W. Daniel Co. 1990.

De Bono, E., *Six Thinking Hats,* London: Penguin 1990.

Dougherty, T.J., 'Photosensitisation of malignant tumours' in S. Ecomon, ed., *Adjuncts to Cancer Therapy,* Philadelphia: Lea & Febinger 1980.

Dougherty, T.J., 'Photoradiation Therapy — new approaches', *Seminars in Surgical Oncology,* 6–16.

Gerard, R.M., 'Differential effects of coloured lights on psychophysiological functions. Ph.D. thesis University of California at Los Angeles, 1958.

Gimbel, T., *The Book of Colour Healing,* London: Gaia Books Ltd 1994.

Gurudas, *Gem Elixirs and Vibrational Healing* II, California: San Rafael Press 1986.

Ivanov, A., 'Soviet experiments in eyeless vision', *International Journal of Parapsychology I* 1 (1965), 5–22.

Keenan, B., *An Evil Cradling,* London: Arrow 1993.

Krakov, S.V., 'Colour vision and the nervous system', *Journal of the Optical Society of America* (June 1942).

Lacey, J. R., 'Neonatal jaundice and phototherapy' *Paediatric Clinics of N. America* 19 (4), (1972).

Legwold, G., 'Color-boosted energy: how light affects muscle action', *American Health* (May 1988).

Liberman, J., *Light: Medicine of the Future,* Santa Fe: Bear & Co. 1991.

Liberman, J., 'Light, Medicine of the future', *Caduceus* (Summer 1992), 22–5.

McDonald, S.F., 'Effects of visible light waves on arthritis pain: a controlled study', *International Journal of Biosocial Research* 3, 2 (1982), 49–54.

Motoyama, H. *Theories of the Chakras: Bridge to Higher Consciousness,* Wheaton, Illinois: Theosophical Society Publishing House 1988.

Novomeiskii, *et al.* reported in Ostrander, S. & Schroeder, L.S., *Psychic Discoveries Behind the Iron Curtain,* London: Sphere Books 1973.

Oren, D.A. & Brainard, G.C., 'Treatment of Seasonal Affective Disorder with green and red light', *American Journal of Psychiatry* 148 (4 April 1991).

Ott, J., 'Colour and Light: their effects on plants, animals and people', *Journal of Biosocial Research* 7, part 1 (1985).

Ott, J., *Health and Light: the effects of natural and artificial light on man and other living things,* Cold Greenwich, Conn: Devin-Adair Co. 1973.

Pellegrini, R.J., Schauss, A.G., Birk, T.J., 'Leg strength as a function of exposure to visual stimuli of different hues', *Bulletin of the Psychosomatic Society* 16, 2, 111–12.

Pierrakos, J.C., *Core Energetics,* Mendocino, California: Life Rhythm 1990.

Plack, J.J. & Schick, J., 'The effects of color on human behaviour', *Journal of the Association for the Study of Perception* 9 (1974), 4–16.

Reich, W., *The Function of the Orgasm,* trans. Theodore P. Wolfe, New York: Oregon Institute Press, 1961.

Roney-Dougal, S.M., 'The psychophysiology of the yogic-chakra system', *Caduceus* (1989), 8–11.

Schauss, A.G., 'The physiological effect of color on the suppression of human aggression: Research on Baker-Muller pink', *International Journal of Biosocial Research,* 72 (1985), 55–64.

Schauss, A.G., 'Tranquilising effect of color reduces aggressive behaviour and potential violence', *The Journal of Orthomolecular Psychiatry* 8, 4 (1974), 218–21.

Schwarz, J. *Human Energy Systems,* New York: E.P. Dutton 1980.

Sun, H. & Sun, D., *Colour Your Life,* London: Piatkus 1992.

Vilenskaya, L., 'Studies in skin vision', *applied Psi Newsletter* 1 (May/June 1982).

Wall, P.D., 'The gate-control theory of pain mechanisms: a re-examination and re-statement', *Brain: 191,* 1–18 (1989).

Watson, M., 'Vital force and electricity', *Caduceus* (Autumn 1988), 24–6.

Westlake, A.T., *The Origins and History of Psionic Medicine,* London: Psionic Medical Society 1977.

White, R., 'Rainbows of health', *Caduceus* (Spring 1989).

Wills, P., *Colour Therapy: The use of Colour for Health and Healing,* London: Element Books 1993.

Wohlfarth, H., 'Experiments to assert the effects of color-stimuli upon the autonomic nervous system', *Excerpta Medica Neurology and Psychiatry* 2 (1958).

Index